HELEN BIANCHIN

the savage touch

TORONTO • LONDON • LOS ANGELES • AMSTERDAM
SYDNEY • HAMBURG • PARIS • STOCKHOLM • ATHENS • TOKYO

Harlequin Presents edition published October 1981
ISBN 0-373-10457-X

Original hardcover edition published in 1981
by Mills & Boon Limited

"The perfect husband is a wealthy one."

Lee continued lightly, "Providing he wasn't over fifty, I'd use all my feminine wiles to get him."

"And what would this mythical millionaire whom you intend marrying get in return?" Marc pursued relentlessly.

"My loyalty," she said evenly. "And fidelity." Why were all the guests looking so expectant? Almost as if they knew something that she didn't.

"And you'd marry at short notice?" Marc asked silkily.

"Why would there be any reason to wait?"

"Thank you, Lee," Marc acknowledged mockingly. His dark gleaming eyes swept around the crowded table. "Congratulations are in order, don't you all agree?"

Lee frowned, then demanded, "What do you mean?"

Marc's smile was frankly cynical, his eyes deadly. "You've just agreed to become my wife."

HELEN BIANCHIN
is also the author of these

Harlequin Presents

and these
Harlequin Romances

Many of these titles are available at your local bookseller.

For a free catalogue listing all available Harlequin Romances and Harlequin Presents, send your name and address to:

HARLEQUIN READER SERVICE
1440 South Priest Drive, Tempe, AZ 85281
Canadian address: Stratford, Ontario N5A 6W2

CHAPTER ONE

LEE slipped the strap of her overnight bag from her shoulder and hurried down the aisle, conscious of mild curiosity and an occasional glare of disapproval as she made her way towards the rear of the plane. It was useless to explain to one and all that her taxi, booked several hours earlier, had arrived late, resulting in a dash at breakneck speed to the airport.

Oh, lord, the window seat—it would have to be, wouldn't it, Lee decided with a faint grimace as she located her designated row. It simply wasn't turning out to be her day at all!

The next instant she registered shock as she encountered a pair of male eyes reflecting lazy mockery and something more than casual interest in their slate-grey depths, and her mouth tightened fractionally as the man released his seatbelt and stepped out into the aisle.

Despite her being of average height and wearing four-inch stiletto heels, her eyes barely came level with his throat, and she felt stifled by the height and breadth of him. The faint elusive tang of his aftershave teased her nostrils, and she was made shockingly aware of a latent sexuality that succeeded in bringing all her defensive instincts to the fore.

Perhaps it was an inner anger that caused her to move too quickly, for the next thing she knew she was falling ignominiously against him. Hard hands steadied her, then she was free, and with a breathless apology she quickly slipped into her seat.

His silent appraisal was disturbing, and seconds later she raised startled eyes as he leant towards her.

'Your seatbelt,' he drawled, clipping the offending straps together.

'Thank you,' Lee acknowledged coolly, deliberately not meeting his gaze, and with a determined effort she turned her attention to the scene beyond the window as the powerful jet eased itself away from the loading bay and taxied out to the runway.

Once they were in the air she relaxed somewhat, and accepting a magazine offered by the hostess she flipped through the pages in search of an interesting article.

As much as Lee tried to ignore her companion's presence she was unable to prevent her gaze from occasionally straying in his direction. There was a sense of hidden strength about him, an aura of power that intrigued her, and she mentally labelled him as an interstate businessman in one of the accepted professions, from his apparent absorption with a sheaf of papers extracted from his briefcase soon after take-off.

Upon touch-down at Brisbane airport Lee obediently observed the hostess's instruction that passengers travelling north to Townsville and Cairns were required to wait in the terminal lounge for their connecting flight, and gathering her belongings together she stood to her feet and joined the queue vacating the aircraft.

The skin on her back prickled as all the fine body hairs stood on end in defence of the man standing immediately behind, and she held herself rigidly to prevent the faint shivering sensation that threatened to shake her slim form.

On reaching the ground Lee was aware of the moment he moved past her, and she watched his progress with idle interest. Attired in casual grey trousers and a navy jacket, he exuded powerful masculinity from every nerve and muscle. A superb male animal with all the latent qualities sufficient to quicken the beat of many a female heart—including hers, she perceived wryly.

Inside the terminal building there was barely time to freshen up and attempt to restore order to her hair. Not that it mattered much, Lee decided as she tugged a brush through its unruly length. Of deep auburn and reaching down on to her shoulders, it grew thick with a slight natural wave that had a will of its own, precluding any attempt to subdue it into smoothness. Consequently she adopted a casual windswept style that was the envy of friends who paid exorbitant salon prices to obtain a similar effect.

Lee withdrew a slim compact from her overnight bag and touched a light dusting of powder to her nose, then stood back to inspect the result. It would be all too easy to attach the label of beautiful to her finely-etched features, but she discarded such compliments when given, aware with self-criticism that her eyes merged between hazel and gold in colour and were too large and widely-spaced for the size of her face, and her mouth was a shade too full. As for her nose—it was average in size, but couldn't decide whether to tilt slightly upwards or not, verging somewhere in between. Her figure was reasonable, she conceded reluctantly as she cast it a cursory glance, and lifting a hand she straightened the lapel of the white jacket she wore over a pencil-slim black skirt.

Stepping back from the mirror, Lee caught up her

overnight bag, checked that she had her tickets, then emerged into the departure lounge. There was time for her to purchase a magazine, and she quickly selected two as she heard her connecting flight announced over the loudspeaker. Hurrying quickly through the barrier, she crossed the tarmac and boarded the waiting aircraft ahead of the other passengers. This time she had no intention of being the last to embark.

Immersed in the contents of her magazine, she paid scant attention to her fellow passengers, and she was only vaguely aware when the adjoining seat became occupied.

It was several seconds before she realised that her travelling companion was none other than the forceful rugged-looking man into whose arms she had fallen less than two hours previously. Coincidence was definitely unkind, for now she had little option but to suffer his presence for a further three hours.

Airborne, Lee relaxed her seatbelt and accepted the luncheon tray the hostess placed before her, doing justice to the Danish open sandwich and coffee, before returning her attention to her magazine.

'Do you mind if I smoke?'

Lee turned slightly and met his faintly mocking smile. 'I'd rather you didn't,' she declared coolly, and saw one eyebrow rise in open sardonic query. 'Why not change your seat?' she suggested civilly, and wondered why she was being so contrary. It didn't worry her in the slightest whether he smoked or not. 'I'm sure the hostess would delight in obliging you,' she added as an unveiled barb. Both hostesses had each on two separate occasions paused to enquire if everything was to his satisfaction, their charm ultra-bright. Lee found their attention irritated her unbearably—almost as much as the man himself.

'I daresay I can manage to survive without a cigarette for a few hours,' he managed with droll amusement—in fact his mouth seemed to be working against revealing a smile, and Lee effected a careless shrug as she returned to her magazine.

The plane touched down briefly at Townsville, then began the final leg to Cairns. If Lee had hoped her fellow passenger might have terminated his journey prior to Cairns, she was doomed to be disappointed, although he made no further attempt to claim her attention.

After leaving the cool wintry climes of Sydney only hours before, the warmth of the tropics was something Lee welcomed with open arms—that, and being reunited with her sister, was sufficient to bring a wide smile to her lips, transforming her expression as she welcomed Alicia with a generous hug.

'Where's the tribe?' Lee queried laughingly as she retrieved her luggage, and Alicia gave a deprecating grin.

'I left them with Stefano's mother. Driving down the Kuranda Range with three exuberant little boys is an experience I can well do without. Besides,' the older girl smiled, 'I wanted to get up to date on your affairs.'

Lee lifted an expressive eyebrow and began teasingly, 'Well, there's a television actor, a doctor, and an airline pilot. Not forgetting an executive in real estate. With whom would you like me to begin?' She was merely teasing and knew Alicia was aware of it, but it was doubtful the man immediately behind them took it in that vein.

The first to move away, Alicia brushed against him

and turned with a murmured apology, only to exclaim with recognition. 'Why, Marc—hello!' Her face lit with undisguised pleasure. 'I didn't realise you were due back so soon. Did you have a good trip?'

His rugged features creased into an attractive smile as he acknowledged her greeting. 'Very enjoyable, Alicia.' His dark eyes swept towards Lee with lazy mockery. 'Aren't you going to introduce me?'

'Yes, of course,' Alicia laughed, her gaze frankly mischievous. 'My sister, Lee Carruthers—Marcello Leone.'

Lee inclined her head briefly. 'How do you do,' she murmured formally, then with deliberate disinterest she indicated, 'If you'll excuse me? I must check with the desk and reconfirm my return flight.' The slight was intended, and with a cool smile she turned and slipped into the slowly-moving stream of people crowding the small airport lounge.

What transpired during her absence she had no idea, for when she rejoined Alicia there was no sign of the man.

'Well, what did you think of him?'

Lee was deliberately vague. 'Who?' They had reached the car-park, and she cast a searching glance for the dark blue station wagon her brother-in-law owned. 'Where have you parked the car?'

'Oh really, Lee,' Alicia muttered with an impatient gesture. 'You know very well I mean Marc—and the car is over there.'

It wasn't until they were on the outskirts of Cairns and heading towards the Kuranda Range that Alicia demanded her sister's response, and Lee made a slight grimace of distaste.

'Far too self-assured for my liking.'

'He's dishy,' Alicia argued emphatically, shooting

Lee a sharp glance. 'Honestly, what's wrong with you?'

'He's not my type,' Lee dismissed blandly. 'Besides, I'm a career girl, remember?'

Alicia pursed her lips in frustrated irritation. 'Marc Leone operates one of the most successful tobacco farms in the Far North, as well as having various business interests in Brisbane and Sydney.'

'I presume I'm meant to deduce from that information that he's ideal husband material,' Lee pronounced dryly. 'Sorry, sister dear—he'd have to be a millionaire to interest me.'

'You're still not harbouring that ridiculous notion, are you?' Alicia frowned, and Lee gave a chuckle of amusement.

'They're a scarce commodity these days. And yes,' she paused in contemplation. '*When* I marry, financial security will be my main consideration. We had too many years having to watch every cent for me not to give it priority.'

Alicia concentrated her attention on the narrow winding ascent, handling the large vehicle with competence. 'Well, I trust you'll have the good manners to be polite to Marc,' she said. 'I've invited him to dinner tomorrow night.'

'Alicia, if this is another of your matchmaking campaigns, I swear I'll strangle you!' Lee exploded emotively, and her sister laughed.

'On the contrary,' she grinned, 'Marc is a frequent guest at our house.'

'If he and Stefano are such good friends, why haven't I met him before?'

'Marc travels a lot between each tobacco season,' Alicia answered seriously. 'A manager runs the farm for him, and Marc's involvement is purely that of overseer. His father died several years ago, and his mother alternates her time between her daughter in Sydney, preferring to spend the winter in the north with Marc.'

'Why give me a rundown on his life-history?' Lee queried with a touch of cynicism.

'Because I think he's just the man to bring you to your knees,' her sister responded swiftly.

Lee laughed out loud. 'Oh lord,' she declared rue-fully. 'You're nothing if not brutally honest!'

'It's called sisterly love,' Alicia said complacently.

'Heaven help me!'

For the remainder of the drive they caught up to date on each other's activities, and Lee was scarcely aware of the passing scenery as the station wagon tra-versed the Range. This was her third visit to the tob-acco-growing town of Mareeba, and she was familiar with the terrain, the abundance of bush-clad hills that levelled out on to a plateau where the air was clean and sweet so far above the sea.

Dusk fell swiftly, and a few miles from the township itself the black of night obliterated everything beyond the powerful beam of the vehicle's headlights.

'We're having dinner with my in-laws,' said Alicia as they reduced speed and entered the built-up resi-dential area. 'I hope you don't mind?'

'Why should I mind?' Lee countered. 'They're very charming people.'

'Stefano and his brother, Mario, have been helping their father paint the house, and they insisted we eat there tonight.' Alicia turned off the main road and within minutes brought the station wagon to a halt.

Almost at once the front door of the house opened, and Lee became immersed in greeting three boyish pyjama-clad bundles all vying for her attention.

'All right, you lot,' a faintly-accented male voice drawled. 'Leave your aunt alone for a few minutes!'

Lee met the twinkling gaze of her brother-in-law and reciprocated his greeting with a hug. As they moved indoors a delicious aroma teased her nostrils, and she accepted the glass of wine that was pressed into her hand.

The following few hours Lee found pleasant and relaxing. Italian hospitality was second to none, and a tiny prickle of envy rose to the surface for the loving family her sister had acquired through marriage.

It was after ten when they carried the three small boys out to the station wagon and headed through town to the farm some five miles past the Barron River, and, pleasantly weary from the flight and the combination of good food and wine, Lee elected to unpack only the bare essentials before tumbling into bed.

Never a late sleeper even while on vacation, she rose early the following morning and showered, then gave Alicia a helping hand with the boys. Baby James had his breakfast perched in a high-chair and required constant supervision despite an assertion that he was capable of feeding himself, while Andrew and Steve argued over who had the most fingers of toast to go with their boiled eggs.

'Bedlam!' their mother groaned in mock-horror. 'This one is definitely going to be a girl,' she indicated, patting her stomach, and Lee smiled.

'And if it's not, you'll try again—right?'

'Not on your life,' Alicia vowed goodnaturedly. 'James was supposed to be *Jane*. If I don't win out this time, I shall just give up!'

'Hmm, I'll remind you of that,' Stefano teased darkly, and his wife proffered a sweet smile.

'It's your fault,' she accorded. 'You shouldn't have used subtle persuasion by saying how nice it would be to have a miniature replica of me!'

'Time to take the tractor out of the paddock,' he grinned unrepentantly, and standing to his feet he dropped a kiss on top of his wife's head, smiled at Lee, then gave his offspring a cheery wave and took his leave.

'Typical!' Alicia groaned with mock indignation at his departing back, before casting a rueful glance over the table and the cherubic expressions of her three sons. 'Why do you suppose they manage to get more food on their faces, clothes and the tablecloth than in their mouths?'

Lee laughed, pulling a face at each of her nephews in turn. 'Because they're little piggies, that's why! They don't need bibs, they need shrouds that cover them from neck to ankle.'

'That's a thought,' Alicia pondered. 'Well, I guess we begin mopping-up operations. I'll take James, if you'll fix the other two.'

Preparations for dinner began when the two youngest boys had been put down for their afternoon nap, and as evening drew close Lee began to wish she could invent a prior engagement. Dining with Marc Leone wasn't her idea of enjoyable entertainment, and she deliberately played down her appearance by dressing casually in a blouse and batik skirt, adding only a touch of lipstick and a dusting of powder to her nose before emerging into the kitchen to give her sister some assistance.

'Lee, aren't you going to wear something more'—

Alicia paused and waved a descriptive hand—'elegant?'

'I'm on holiday,' Lee responded wryly. 'Being elegantly attired doesn't figure largely on my list of priorities.'

Her sister shot her a particularly perceptive look before turning back to attend to the numerous saucepans on top of the kitchen stove. 'You don't want to bedazzle Marc, having decided you don't like him,' she announced, and Lee gave a careless shrug.

'He doesn't affect me one way or the other, and if you really object to my clothes I'll go and change them.'

'Lee!' Alicia protested ruefully. 'You're one of the few fortunate people who would manage to look glamorous in sackcloth. It's just that I——'

'You want to me to make an impression, right?'

'Yes,' Alicia agreed with engaging frankness. 'Marc is a gorgeous hunk of masculinity, and you're my one and only sister. It would be fantastic if you were to marry someone from these parts—then we'd be close together, instead of living at opposite ends of Australia.'

Lee extracted a tablecloth from a nearby dresser and began setting the large dining-room table. 'You know my views on marriage. One day—*maybe*. I want to travel, live a little before settling down with one man and a life of mundane chores.'

'It has its advantages,' Alicia defended dryly, and Lee laughed.

'I've yet to be convinced of that.'

'Convinced of what?' a familiar male voice queried, and she turned to meet Stefano's teasing smile, her features assuming a polite mask as she saw his companion.

'Alicia and I were having a discussion,' she answered blandly, and silently dared her to enlighten the two men.

'You have met, I believe?' Stefano indicated, swinging an interested gaze from Lee back to Marc Leone.

'Yesterday,' Marc drawled indolently. 'We travelled on the same flight.' His frame seemed to diminish the room's proportions, although he wasn't much taller than Stefano. His attire was casual, yet he still managed to exude a sophistication that was more akin to city living. Evident too was a leashed quality and a measure of cynicism that in different circumstances Lee would have found fascinating.

Forced to acknowledge him, she proffered a slight smile. 'Mr Leone.' She didn't add any superfluous platitudes, and met his gaze with deliberate coolness.

'Marcello,' he insisted silkily. 'My friends call me Marc.'

'How nice,' Lee responded sweetly, then turning back to the dresser she began extracting plates and cutlery.

'Have Mario and Lisa arrived yet?' Alicia queried, directing her husband a faintly flustered look.

'Now, from the sound of it,' Stefano answered calmly. 'Marc and I will drag Mario into the lounge for a drink while you womenfolk organise the food.'

Do that, Lee echoed silently. The less time she had to spend in Marc Leone's company, the better.

If it hadn't have been for Lisa and Mario's company the evening would have been something of a disaster. Lee utilised every opportunity to assist Alicia in serving the food, entered into conversation with the notable exception of Marc Leone, which didn't seem to bother him a whit, although there was one occasion when the slate-grey gaze met hers with disturbing scrutiny, and much to her chagrin she was the first to glance away.

'How long do you intend to stay up north?'

Lee glanced across the table at the sound of that sardonic drawl, and summoned forth a cool smile. 'Three weeks,' she answered in faintly bored tones, and saw his eyes darken fractionally.

'Perhaps you'll allow me to show you something of the area during your stay,' he offered, and Alicia pounced on the suggestion with the tenacity of a terrier being tossed a meaty bone.

'Marc, how good of you,' she acknowledged with sickening gratitude. 'Stefano has to disc-harrow the paddocks and lay the pipes, so there won't be much time to spare for sightseeing.'

'My pleasure,' he accorded civilly, swinging his attention back to Lee. 'Shall we say tomorrow?'

'I wouldn't think of inconveniencing you, Mr Leone,' Lee refused sweetly, giving his name slight emphasis. 'You've just returned from a trip abroad. Surely you have more important things to do?' Her eyes were deliberately lacking in guile.

'I can spare a few days,' he answered sardonically, and she noted that his eyes were far from indolent. If he could, he would have shaken her and taken pleasure from the exercise, Lee thought with a faint shiver.

'It's kind of you to offer,' she began politely. 'But I want to spend as much time as I can with my sister.'

'Nonsense, Lee,' Alicia protested. 'You must go.'

'Must I?' she challenged with a smile. 'I'm sure Mr Leone will understand if I refuse.' She turned towards him. 'Won't you?'

'No,' he drawled, and her eyes widened in startled disbelief. 'Shall we say nine tomorrow morning?'

Of all the nerve! Anger turned her eyes into a fiery gold, but there was little she could do other than capitulate, and she did so with apparent graciousness. Although there was the promise of retaliation in the glance she shot him as he took his leave some hours later. If it was war he wanted, then that was what he would get!

CHAPTER TWO

'HAVE a nice day.'

Lee directed her sister a wry glance as she slipped into the passenger seat of Marc Leone's large Ford Fairlane. The prospect of an entire day spent in his company was something she viewed with the antithesis of enjoyment. 'Thanks,' she acknowledged with marked irony. 'See you later.'

'Around five,' Marc confirmed, his smile warm as he sketched Alicia a wave, then he slid in behind the wheel and set the engine purring into life.

Within seconds the powerful car had traversed the drive and was picking up speed on the open road, heading towards Mareeba, and it wasn't until they were almost at Kuranda that Lee decided to question their intended destination.

'Where are you taking me?' Her voice was cool, barely a point or two above an arctic zero, and his swift glance raked her with an intensity that was nerve-racking.

'As you're determined not to enjoy yourself, does it matter?'

Lee sat erect in her seat. 'We don't like each other.'

'On what basis do you make that assumption?'

'Oh, for heaven's sake!' Lee expostulated. 'Whatever motivated this invitation, it wasn't mutual empathy.'

'How about—you intrigue me?' Marc drawled, and she uttered a brief harsh laugh.

'So unoriginal. I must have heard that at least a hundred times.'

'Like bees, the men flit around the honeypot,' he drawled with marked cynicism, and she arched him a saccharine smile.

'Let's just say I'm aware of all the angles.'

'Really?'

His sardonic amusement rankled. 'Do you doubt it?' she levelled coolly, and she became incensed by the undisguised mockery evident in his eyes. 'Are you bored, or just deliberately obtuse?' she demanded angrily.

'With hair that colour, you couldn't possess anything less than a shameful temper.'

The look she gave him would have withered a lesser man on the spot. 'If you'll be so good as to stop the car, I'll hitch a ride back. Another minute in your company and I'm liable to resort to violence!'

'Be warned that I hit back,' Marc asserted with quiet deliberation. 'Why not take in the passing scenery? Soon we'll be down the Range and into sugarcane country.'

'Spare me the lyrical spiel. I'm not one of your impressionable dates, willing to hang on to your every word,' she snapped angrily.

'Are you usually so—hostile? The man who took

you on would need to be a hardy individual.'

'I'm usually quite calm,' Lee declared, her voice moving up a pitch. 'And I don't need any man to take me on, as you so charmingly put it!'

'All that fine fury,' he mused. 'It could prove a challenge, at that.'

'My God! I wouldn't touch you with a ten-foot pole!'

'Did you have breakfast?' he slanted mildly, and his amusement was almost her undoing.

'Of course. Why?'

An eyebrow ascended in silent mockery. 'Not one of the crispbread and black coffee brigade?'

'I have a healty appetite,' she informed him with an expressive sigh, and the eyebrow rose even further.

'It's not lack of food that's responsible for your ill-humour?'

'No, dammit—it's *you*!' she shouted, and became utterly incensed when he laughed. 'Let me out. I'm not going another mile with you!'

'Yes, you are,' Marc insisted quietly, and she threw him a venomous look.

'I'm not. Now, stop this wretched vehicle!'

Without another word he slowed down and drew to a halt at the edge of the road, letting the engine idle, and with an angry toss of her head Lee unlatched the door-clasp and slid out, giving the door a satisfactory slam.

The thought of hitching a ride was slightly daunting, but pride lifted her head as she moved round behind the car and crossed to the other side of the road. To be honest, she hadn't expected him to call her bluff, and now that he had she felt vaguely apprehensive.

After she had walked a few yards came the thought that she would have to explain to Alicia precisely why she was returning several hours earlier than expected, and alone. Damn—the ensuing argument wasn't something she looked forward to.

'Get in.'

Lee swung round and saw that Marc had backed the car, and it was now stationary directly opposite. For a moment she almost relented, but stubborn pride won out and she continued walking.

'Whether you get in of your own accord or not is immaterial,' Marc's voice directed hardily.

Lee ignored him, glancing back in the hope that another car would appear, but the road was disappointingly empty, and she increased her stride as she heard the snap of the car door. Not that it mattered much, for even if she ran he would soon outdistance her.

'You are the most exasperating female I have ever met,' his voice commented bluntly from immediately behind, and the next instant she was brought to an abrupt halt as his hand fastened on her arm in a bone-crushing grip. 'You've had time to cool down—now come and get back in the car.'

'Leave me alone!'

Marc muttered something unintelligible, then without warning he hoisted her over his shoulder and carried her indignant wildly-kicking form across the road.

'You fiend!' Lee cried, beating angry fists against his back. 'Put me down!'

Within seconds she was bundled into the front seat of the car, then Marc slid in beside her, and his expression sent prickles of alarm scudding down her spine.

'If you've finished behaving like a spoilt ill-mannered child, maybe we can continue on our way,' he declared with chilling brusqueness, and her hand went to the door-clasp only to discover it was locked and wouldn't release.

'Let me out!' she demanded furiously, rounding on him. 'If you don't unlock this damned door, I swear I'll scream my head off!'

'Go ahead.'

Without thinking her hand flew up and struck his face, then she uttered a startled cry as he calmly slapped her back.

'You—bastard!' Lee choked, her eyes alive with rage. 'That hurt!' She raised a hand to her stinging cheek, unable to believe he had actually struck her.

'It was meant to,' Marc responded with icy imperturbability.

'I hate you,' she whispered, and he gave a careless shrug.

'At least that's a fairly healthy emotion.'

Balling her fist, she aimed it at that arrogant jaw, only to fail dismally as he caught hold of her wrist in mid-air.

'Oh no, you don't,' he said in a dangerously soft voice. Exerting pressure, he pulled her towards him until her face was within touching distance of his own, then with deliberate intent he lowered his mouth to hers.

There wasn't a thing Lee could do to stop him, and the cry that rose to her lips died in her throat as his mouth crushed hers in a kiss that plundered to the very depths of her soul. She was completely at his mercy, and there was one brief horrifying moment when she thought she might slip into the dark void that threatened her consciousness, for never had she been made so frighteningly aware of a man's latent savagery.

Her mouth quivered in pain when at last he lifted his head, and there was real fear in her eyes for an instant before the lids shuttered down.

'Look at me.' His brusque command held a ruthlessness that boded ill for anyone daring to thwart him. His eyes darkened fractionally at her downbent head, and without a word he caught her chin between thumb and forefinger and forced her into obedience. 'You could goad a man to the very brink of sanity,' he muttered with ruminative pitilessness. 'Be thankful I retain a firm hold on mine.'

It took courage to meet his gaze, even more to utter as a last gesture of defiance, 'Am I supposed to bow down in gratitude?'

'And acknowledge defeat?' he queried sardonically, then his voice hardened measurably. 'Be warned I'm no loser, Lee.'

'What's that supposed to mean?'

'I imagine you possess sufficient intelligence to work it out for yourself.' With a quick glance in the rear vision mirror he eased the powerful car back on to the road, picking up speed as he took the coast road leading to Mossman via Ellis Beach.

Lee was too emotionally drained to consider making polite conversation, and the thought of the whole day in his company was galling. A faint bubble of hysterical laughter rose in her throat. Unless she was mistaken she had just been given her first lesson in submission. If that was the case, Marc Leone was in for a surprise! She had no intention of being beneath any

man's thumb—much less *his*. The whole thing was
ludicrous, especially as she found him detestable and
far too high-handed for his own good. If she didn't
speak to him at all then they couldn't argue, and with
that in mind she turned to admire the scenery.

A vast patchwork of green canefields and dark-red
ploughed land provided a startling contrast to the
bush-clad ranges around whose base the ribbon of
bitumen followed the coast. Narrow steel railway
tracks criss-crossed the Captain Cook highway with
predictable frequency as they linked each farm to the
main line.

'The cane is burnt off in workable sections to get rid
of undergrowth and any vermin,' Marc told her
smoothly. 'It is mechanically harvested, then loaded
on to wagons and transported for processing to the
Mill.'

Lee inclined her head slightly in deference, and refrained from telling him that she was already aware of
the process, having travelled this particular route with
Alicia and Stefano two years ago.

As the car swung down the winding incline towards
Ellis Beach Marc leaned forward and switched on the
car radio, and Lee welcomed the intrusion.

Sparkling blue water stretched out towards the horizon, merging into the azure sky. Queensland was
truly a sunshine State, and the winterless North
nothing less than a tropical paradise. At this time of
year it was relatively easy to disregard the enervating
heat of summer, the flies and mosquitoes. Summer
also brought intermittent rainstorms, and the onset of
the Wet where the continuous rainfall for several
weeks on end was sufficient to fray even the mildest of
tempers.

'The work here is seasonal,' Marc continued imperturbably. 'Cane, from June until December—tobacco concentrating between September and March, although the farmer has to prepare the ground, the seedbeds, then plant out prior to that. However, between April and August he can relax, working maybe as few as two days a week checking equipment and machinery.'

Lee didn't bother to comment, and for the following half hour she sat in contemplative silence. If her lack of conversation bothered him, Marc gave no indication, and it wasn't until he turned the car off the main highway that she voiced her surprise.

'Where are we going?'

'You've decided to speak,' Marc commented dryly, and she cast him a wry glance.

'Sarcasm, Mr Leone?'

'What were thinking of?' he countered cynically. 'Or should I amend that to *who*?'

The smile she gave him was singularly sweet. 'Oh, who—of course.'

'Ah, yes,' he said dryly. 'An actor, an airline pilot—among others, I believe.'

So he had overheard her! 'Shouldn't I have a boyfriend?' she posed, and he gave an indolent shrug.

'I imagine they fight each other to get to your door.'

'Oh, the pathway is inevitably a veritable battlefield,' she answered with droll humour.

'No wedding ring as yet?'

'A symbol of bondage?' she queried with deliberate sarcasm. 'That's not for me.'

'Pity,' Marc drawled, and she shot him a dark glance, only to find that he was seemingly intent on the road ahead. 'Precisely what do you do for a living?'

he questioned after several minutes, casting her a brief searching glance.

'I'm a hair-stylist.'

'With visions of owning your own salon, I presume?'

Lee was aware of his cynical amusement, and it rankled. 'What's wrong with that?' she demanded. 'Although I doubt you would approve of a woman pursuing a career, would you?'

'Why not add—being a male chauvinist?' Marc intoned with deliberate mockery, and she gave him a sweet smile.

'I was going to.'

The car slowed perceptively, then veered off to the right towards Port Douglas.

'There are women for whom marriage and children would prove disastrous,' he slanted, 'but you're not one of them.'

'Oh? On what premise do you base that assumption?'

'Have you never looked in the mirror?' he mocked brusquely. 'One day you'll come up against a man who'll——'

'Sweep me off my feet?' she interrupted with a derisive laugh. 'Oh, come on—you don't believe in that romantic nonsense any more than I do!'

'I was going to say—bed you, then put a ring on your finger before you had time to think about it,' he concluded bluntly.

Lee felt her stomach lurch in an unaccustomed somersault. 'Haven't you got that the wrong way round?' she managed lightly.

'Bridal purity is a rare jewel,' he stated hardily. 'Most men no longer seek it.' His quick glance was dark and unfathomable.

'The double standard,' Lee retorted with heavy sarcasm. 'You're no monk,' she accused. 'Why enforce celibacy on women?'

'That's a touchy subject I've no intention of pursuing while driving,' he answered, and she rounded on him with unaccustomed bitterness.

'How typical of a male to cop out!'

Marc slowed the car as they neared the small township, then turned towards the beach and drew to a halt on the grass verge. He made no move to get out, and she eyed him rather warily as he leaned towards her.

'Okay, so let's argue,' he berated uncompromisingly. 'It's the one thing we seem to do well.'

'Don't we just,' Lee agreed, overcome by his nearness. All her protective instincts told her to get out and run as fast and as far away from this disturbing man as her legs would carry her. He was dangerous, and totally unlike anyone she had ever met before. The usual tactics she employed with other men were proving to be ineffective.

'You were saying?' Marc prompted, his manner deceptively mild, and Lee gave a sudden inexplicable shiver as she met his eyes. Their expression was far from indolent.

'I need some fresh air,' she declared lightly, and he gave a deep throaty chuckle.

'Oh, Lee,' he chided with amusement, 'I'm disappointed. I thought we were about to do battle.'

Her lips moved in a wry grimace. 'I still retain a vivid memory of the last one.'

He regarded her in silence, then reaching out a hand he traced her mouth with a light probing finger, then his head moved towards hers, and her lips parted to plead, except that it was too late—way too late.

Beneath that firm insistent pressure she put up a token resistance, then closed her eyes as he began a sensual exploratory invasion of her mouth. Her senses leapt, flaring into warmth, and she gave a silent moan as his hands slid round her neck and buried themselves in the tangled thickness of her hair. His experience was devastating, and she had to force herself not to respond, for therein lay madness—a madness she neither wanted nor could afford.

At last he lifted his head, his expression inscrutable as he regarded her in silence, then he smiled as he released her. 'Let's walk along the beach and work up an appetite for lunch.'

Without a word Lee reached for the door-clasp and slid out from the car.

The tide was on the way out, and without seeing whether Marc would follow she slipped off her sandals and stepped down on to the crisp white sand. A faint breeze stirred her hair and teased the hemline of her dress as she walked. Her lips still tingled, and a slow-burning rage rose in her breast. In the past it had been she who held the whip-hand in any relationship, and it angered her beyond belief to be so easily set down. She uttered a brief soundless laugh. What was she thinking? She no more had any intention of beginning a relationship with Marc Leone than she had of flying to the moon!

'You live in Sydney?'

'Yes,' Lee answered cursorily, not really wanting to talk to him at all, and she missed his faint smile.

'Have you any family, apart from Alicia?'

She turned and glared at him. 'What is this—question and answer time?'

'Is it forbidden to make conversation?' he parried dryly, and she swung her gaze out to sea.

'My life history is very dull, Mr Leone.'

'Marc,' his voice insisted—commanded would be a better word, and Lee grimaced.

'Don't you ever give up?'

'No.' His quiet denial sent an involuntary shiver of fear feathering the length of her spine.

'I'm twenty-two years old,' Lee told him with no pretence at forbearance, 'born and bred in the city to parents who had long given up on having children. Alicia was a complete surprise, and my appearance eight years later an added bonus. Unfortunately my mother's health suffered soon after my birth, and slowly deteriorated. She died when I was ten. Dad followed her four years later,' she said slowly, her chin tilting slightly. 'It was Alicia and I against the world, with no other relatives to care or look after us. Alicia married and moved north when I was almost seventeen,' she concluded, unwilling to reveal just how lonely that first year apart had really been.

'Do you flat alone?'

'No,' she denied wryly. 'I share a house with three friends.'

'Male or female?'

'One female and two male.' It gave her great satisfaction to impart that information.

'Convenient,' Marc commented dryly, and she gave him a sweet smile.

'Yes, isn't it?'

'I suppose you style men's hair, too.'

'Of course. Most hairdressing salons have adopted the unisex approach. Why?' she queried, shooting him a swift analytical glance. 'Do you need a haircut?' The sarcasm was deliberate, and didn't go undetected.

'Dare I trust you?'

'I'm a professional,' Lee declared angrily. 'I don't allow personalities to affect my work. Anyway,' she added wrathfully, 'I wouldn't do your hair no matter how much you paid me!'

'How paradoxical,' Marc drawled, and she looked away, too infuriated to reply.

The natural shoreline curved, creating a bay that was scenically picturesque, although Lee was in no mood to appreciate its beauty. The man strolling at her side stirred every unenviable emotion she possessed, and although she had had independence forced upon her at an early age she had never before had contact with anyone quite like Marc Leone. By now most men of her acquaintance would have been frozen off by her chilly manner, but he seemed to regard her much as a superior cat biding its time with a recalcitrant mouse. A slight glimmer of humour momentarily lit her eyes. Perhaps if she applied reverse psychology and plied apparent adoration? It would never work, she discounted silently. He was far too astute not to recognise the ploy, and besides, it would only serve to arouse his amusement.

'We'll turn back and have lunch,' Marc indicated, and Lee cast him a searching look.

'I guess the reason you're so arrogant is a surfeit of responsive women willing to bow down to your every wish,' she declared waspishly, and his teeth gleamed as his mouth curved into a mocking smile.

'Of which you're not one,' he said cynically.

'I can't stand you,' she retorted. 'Why on earth I came out with you today I'll never know!'

'I didn't give you much choice.'

'None,' she answered trenchantly, stopping in her tracks. 'I like to be asked, not—forced into something I don't want.' Her eyes darkened, their gleaming depths becoming a fascinating mixture of hazel flecked with dark gold. 'Go and practise your caveman tactics on someone else,' she snapped furiously. 'I don't appreciate them!'

His eyes regarded her solemnly, and his silence was enervating. 'What do you appreciate, Lee? Soft music, dimmed lighting, and a gentle touch?' His faint smile held worldly cynicism. 'I think not. There's too much fire beneath the surface for you to be content with docile ineffectuality.'

Her features lit with fine fury, her chin tilting to a dangerous angle as she rounded on him. 'Oh? On the basis of two days' acquaintance you presume to know my taste in men?' she exclaimed. 'Well, let me tell you that arrogant overbearing bossy men such as yourself come well down on my list. I don't enjoy being on the receiving end of brutal savagery!'

One eyebrow arched in quizzical amusement. 'My, my,' he derided quietly. 'It's apparent you missed out on a few badly needed parental spankings. A word of warning, Lee—don't continue to hand it out unless you're prepared to take the consequences.'

'I shake at the very thought!'

'So you should,' Marc chided softly. 'I'm no pubescent youth with whom you can play childish games.'

'What games do you play?' she challenged sweetly. 'The bedroom variety, I'll be bound. Do you keep a tally of all the broken-hearted females you've carelessly cast aside? Or perhaps they number too many to remember?'

For a moment Lee thought he meant to strike her,

then she was fighting wildly as his arms dragged her relentlessly close, and she struggled valiantly to evade the cruel touch of his mouth as it sought and found her own, punishing with ruthless force until she sagged limply against him. Yet still he ravaged the softness of her mouth, and not content, he trailed a searing path down the pulsing cord at her neck to the base of her throat before travelling up to take her lips with pitiless disregard.

She was unable to move, caught close against him in a painful grip so that she was aware of every muscle in his powerful body, and the hand that held her head paid little heed to her delicate scalp. It seemed unending, and she was almost in tears when the pressure eased, then she gave an involuntary shiver as his lips took on a seducing quality.

An answering flame stirred deep inside, and she was powerless to resist a response that rose of its own accord and encompassed her entire being. She was mindless, with no thought for what she might be inviting, as of their own volition her fingers curled deep into the thick hair at the back of his neck. Like a flower opening its heart to the morning sun her mouth parted and clung to his, and desire flared as his hands began a practised exploration over her slim curves.

There was no thought of denying him as his fingers sought and found the buttons on her dress, and she gave a gasp of pleasure when the garment was no longer a barrier to his touch. He was in complete control as she pressed her body close against him, and she gave a slight moan of distress as he lifted his head.

'Marc?' The slightly breathless query held a dazed quality that sounded strangely bereft, and he smiled, brushing her burgeoned breasts with gentle fingers.

'Not here,' he murmured, his eyes dark as he regarded her, then he lowered his head and gently trailed his lips across her forehead. 'Let's go.'

Lee was still in a state of bemusement. 'Go where?'

His hands moved to the front of her dress and he began fastening the buttons. 'This beach is fairly isolated, but I prefer to conduct my lovemaking in privacy and comfort,' he told her softly, his eyes tinged with mocking amusement. 'There's a motel nearby where we can book a unit for a few hours.'

Oh God! Like a dash of cold water his words brought Lee back to harsh reality, and with it came shame. Shame, and a sense of painful degradation.

'No.' Was that her voice? A husky denial that sounded alien even to her own ears.

Marc's gaze was disconcertingly level. 'No?' he queried deliberately. 'A few minutes ago I was getting a definite yes.'

A mortifying warmth coloured her cheeks. She searched for a flippant reply, but nothing came to mind, and after several seconds she turned away from him and stared sightlessly out over the ocean. Even anger was noticeably absent. What could she say—that she was sorry? It seemed ludicrous to explain that this was the first time she had allowed any man to take such liberties with her body. In the past she had always been in control of a situation, never losing her head and able to reject any amorous advances without much difficulty. Yet for a short while she had been transported beyond the realms of reality into a world of sensual pleasure where nothing registered except the magic of the moment.

Tears rose to the surface and her lips quivered in the knowledge that she didn't even *like* the man. They struck sparks off each other at every turn.

Lee gave a sudden start as his hand caught hold of her arm, and she offered no resistance as he turned her back to face him.

His eyes narrowed fractionally as he glimpsed her expression, and reaching out, he placed an idle finger beneath her chin and lifted it until she met his gaze.

'No fine fury, Lee?' he queried with faint mockery, and she moved out of his grasp.

'I'm temporarily lost for words,' she offered wryly, fighting to regain her composure.

'There's an excellent seafood restaurant round by the harbour,' he declared evenly. 'We'll eat there.'

Food? The thought of it sickened her, but it was important that he shouldn't be aware of just how badly shaken she was, and in order to present an unruffled façade she would eat evey mouthful.

They walked in silence, and Lee paused momentarily when they reached the grass verge beside the road to slip on her sandals. It wasn't until they were almost past the hotel that she ventured anything by way of conversation.

'Alicia mentioned that you've just returned from a trip abroad,' she began with distant politeness. 'Where did you go?'

'Europe—Italy, France, Germany,' Marc elaborated blandly. 'We also spent some time in England, then touched down briefly in Singapore—a total of four months in all.'

'I imagine you enjoyed yourself.' Oh, why couldn't she be more natural, instead of acting like a stiff affronted prude?

His glance held faint mockery. 'I have made similar trips in the past.'

'A well-seasoned traveller,' Lee commented, and he gave a brief sardonic nod.

The restaurant was little more than an unpretentious café, but the food was well presented and lived up to Marc's recommendation. By the time Lee had consumed the first course some of her former antagonism for the man seated opposite had returned, and with it a deep burning anger at his high-handedness. After today she would refuse to have anything more to do with him, and if Alicia continued her matchmaking campaign it would be to no avail, as Lee intended bowing out of any subsequent invitations that included Marc Leone. On that point she would be adamant!

After lunch Marc mentioned that there was a shell collection well worth viewing, and without waiting for her acquiescence he calmly led her past a small group of shops to the house in question. Lee pursed her lips as she accompanied him—not that she had much choice with her arm caught firmly in a grip that threatened to tighten painfully should she dare to resist.

The look she thrust him left him in no doubt as to her feelings, but his expression was grimly set and unyielding. Childishly she wanted to wrench away from his grasp and give vent to a display of unladylike wrath. Only the presence of others, presumably tourists like herself, stopped her.

With grim determination Lee set out to cultivate an interest in the valuable collection, noting that several varieties had been collected from the ocean beds of the Great Barrier Reef. However, the vast majority comprised the work of a lifetime of collecting and collating, involving correspondence throughout the world.

It was mid-afternoon when Marc headed the sleek car back on to the road that led towards the main highway. Lee expected him to head back via the coast, but he turned in the direction of Mossman, thus destroying her hopes for a speedy return to Mareeba.

'I'd like to go home, if you don't mind. I seem to have developed a shocking headache,' she invented, deliberately glancing ahead, and was incensed by his mocking response.

'Had enough?'

'Of you—*yes*!'

'Pity,' he accorded dryly. 'I have some friends I intend visiting in Mossman.'

'You're the most hateful man I've ever had the misfortune to meet,' Lee declared with thinly-veiled bitterness.

'Why? Because I don't pander to your every wish?'

Her laugh held harsh fury. 'You seem to delight in opposing me!'

'What a coincidence,' Marc drawled. 'That's exactly what I think of you.'

'After today, I hope I never see you again!'

'Unlikely.'

'Why?' Lee demanded, and the glance he directed her held wry humour.

'Mareeba is a farming community where everyone knows everyone else,' he slanted. 'I know of at least three occasions within the next week where we're bound to meet.'

'Not if I can help it!'

An eyebrow rose quizzically. 'And risk offending your sister and brother-in-law—not to mention their friends? I think not.'

'I'll develop a headache—an illness—anything,' Lee declared. 'Babysit the children. Wherever it is I'm supposed to be, I won't be there.'

'You will,' Marc evinced pitilessly, and she had to physically refrain from hitting him.

'I'm a free agent. No one can make me do anything I don't want to!'

'You'll selfishly destroy Alicia's plans?' he queried insistently. 'Place her in the awkward position of having to explain your absence at something arranged solely for your benefit?'

Never in her entire life could she remember being so angry. Her fine eyes gleamed with it. 'If—*when*,' she amended resentfully, 'we meet, I'd appreciate it if you will leave me alone!'

'My dear Lee,' Marc drawled, 'you almost sound afraid. Are you?'

'Why should I be?' she demanded wrathfully.

'Admire the scenery,' he advised with evident amusement. 'It's infinitely safer than continuing an argument you have no hope of winning.'

'Oh—go to hell!'

'Be careful I don't take you with me.'

The words were lightly delivered, but Lee strove to control an icy shiver that feathered its way down her spine. Marc Leone was a law unto himself, unpredictable and totally unlike any man she had ever met.

Contrarily she became a polite companion during their brief visit to Mossman, appearing so subdued that Marc's eyes narrowed in silent speculation on more than one occasion before they took their leave and drove towards Mareeba via Biboohra and Mount Molloy. Even then she spoke only when required, and as briefly as possible.

His voiced thanks the instant the car drew to a halt beside the sprawling dwellings that comprised Stefano's farm were brief and totally lacking in sincerity, and she didn't glance back once as she made her way indoors.

CHAPTER THREE

THE two boys were seated at the table busily engaged in demolishing the contents of their plates as Lee entered the dining room, and their shouts of joy at her arrival were seconded by the faintly harassed but smiling inquisitive glance from their mother.

'You're just in time to rescue me from a moment of sheer insanity,' Alicia grinned in welcome. 'Feeding time at the zoo has no parallel to mealtimes in this household!' Her face assumed an anxious expression as she made a lightning grab for baby James' plate which he'd decided to launch into space. 'See what I mean?' she groaned in despair, and Lee shook a mock fist at the infant chuckling merrily in his high chair.

'Naughty grub,' Lee admonished as she knelt to scoop up the sticky indistinguishable remains from the floor. 'Any more of those antics, young man, and we'll remove you outside to eat with the animals!'

James burst into a gale of giggles at this unlikelihood, and beamed cherubically at his mother as she removed his bib and cleaned his face and hands.

'Into the playpen with you, my man,' Alicia accorded, and promptly followed words with action, then shooed the two older boys into the bathroom to wash up and brush their teeth.

'Now,' she turned to face her sister. 'We've half an hour before Stefano comes in from the paddock. Tell me all about it,' she begged.

'About what?' Lee countered calmly, much to her sister's disgust.

'Oh, *Lee*,' Alicia groaned. 'Stop being so darned vague! You know very well what I'm talking about.'

Trying to evade Alicia in such a mood was akin to avoiding an avalanche while standing directly in its path—impossible. It was far better to take the bull by the horns, Lee decided with a faint grimace. 'We drove down to Cairns, then on to Port Douglas,' she said lightly. 'We had lunch there, visited some friends of Marc's in Mossman, then came home via Mount Molloy.'

'And Marc?' Alicia persisted. 'Did he ask you out again?'

'No,' Lee answered coolly. 'And even if he had, I would have refused. He's too sure of himself by half,' she added with some heat. 'Quite frankly, I never want to see him again.'

'Unlikely,' Alicia commented wryly. 'His farm lies less than a mile from here, bordering the main road. He frequently calls in to see us, and besides, in a community as small as ours it would be impossible to avoid him.' She gave Lee an anxious glance. 'You're not going to be difficult, are you?'

'What do you mean?'

'There's a wedding on Saturday. Marc's bound to be a guest,' Alicia revealed slowly. 'And early next week Marc is giving a barbecue in honour of a friend of his who's been overseas for several years. He extended the invitation last night, and mentioned that it was to include you. If you don't come, you'll offend him,' she finished in a rush, and Lee gave a disbelieving laugh.

'Offend Marc Leone? He possesses a hide as thick as a rhinoceros! Totally impregnable.'

'You will come, won't you?' Alicia insisted, and Lee gave a sigh that defied description.

'I daresay I can manage to ignore him,' she conceded, knowing it would be impossible. Marc was a force unto himself, possessing a brand of virile masculinity that created an aura all its own, from which no female heart was immune.

A fact which was brought home with a thudding jolt the following evening, much to Lee's annoyance, although she hid it well. Stefano's parents were far too nice to offend, and consequently she went out of her way to be pleasant.

'Have some more wine, Lee,' Mr Brascetti insisted jovially, leaning forward to refill her glass, and glancing at her near-empty plate moved his hand to encompass the table and its contents. 'Chicken? Risotto? Salad? Which can I help you with?'

'The salad, please,' Lee declared with a smile, and he gave a hearty chuckle.

'Come—you are too thin. Have another piece of chicken, hm?' He cast Marc a twinkling glance. 'We men like to feel we have a woman in our arms, not a collection of skin and bone. Isn't that so, Marcello?'

It took considerable effort for Lee to maintain her expression, and the swift glance she spared in Marc's direction only served to heighten her indignation. Damn him! He was amused, she could tell.

'I find Lee's physical attributes quite satisfactory,' he drawled, and goaded almost beyond endurance she offered with seeming sweetness,

'Most men are wary of women with auburn hair. They're afraid they mightn't be able to handle the fiery temper they imagine must go with it.' She smiled to lessen the sting, aware that everyone else was amused.

'I am not "most men",' Marc declared quietly, his own smile nowhere near reaching his eyes, and she felt a chill scud icily down her spine in warning premonition. He had already proved just how well he could handle her, and the knowledge irked unbearably.

Lee injected just the right amount of awed surprise into her voice. 'My goodness! In what way are you—different?'

'I don't play games.'

She arched an eyebrow in musing contemplation. 'Really? For a professed non-participant, you appear to be in good physical condition.'

'It wasn't sport I was referring to,' Marc retorted with droll cynicism, thus earning a burst of laughter from Stefano and his father, and causing Lee to parry outrageously,

'I didn't imagine for a minute that you were.'

The answering look in his eyes was quickly veiled, and she was grateful not to be alone with him. His vengeance would be swift and deadly, and she wasn't at all sure she had escaped.

'Checkmate?' he offered smoothly, his movements slow and unhurried as he lifted the delicately stemmed wineglass to his lips, sipping a generous quantity with the deliberate savouring action of a connoisseur.

It wasn't polite to answer as she would have liked, so Lee summoned forth a friendly smile and gave a husky laugh, spreading her hands in a gesture of condescension. 'Oh, yes,' she agreed, then giving an irrepressible grin, she reached out and helped herself to some chicken. 'I am hungry after all.'

Marc Leone's presence was something of a surprise. Good friend of the Brascetti family he might be, but he was hardly family. His inclusion for dinner could have been motivated by something as innocuous as a desire to even the numbers sitting at the table, but Lee doubted it. Alicia, bless her heart, was launching an all-out offensive in the matchmaking stakes, having decided Marc to be the number one contestant, and was not above enlisting the help of her mother-in-law to achieve results.

'Oh, Lee,' Alicia's voice broke into Lee's self-imposed reverie, causing her to glance across the wide table. 'You mustn't forget to give me your recipe for *coq au vin*. Stefano has asked me twice in the past few months to make it, but somehow I've mislaid the one you gave me. Then I can copy it out for Mrs Brascetti.'

'Please, Lee,' that good woman endorsed smilingly. 'I would appreciate it.'

Oh, the indignity of it all! Lee inwardly squirmed. The attempt to bring her culinary skills to Marc's notice was blatant to say the least, and totally unforgivable. Beneath a slight smile she directed her sister a killing glance that promised a reckoning at a more appropriate time, then acquiesced in a bland voice.

'You can cook?'

Lee shifted her gaze towards Marc, and after a momentary deliberation she inclined her head. 'Yes,' she answered mockingly. 'It's a hobby of mine.'

'Lee got honours in her class,' Alicia accorded with hapless disregard for her sister's dark glance.

'Hardly the preferred pastime of a self-professed

career woman,' Marc slanted, his tone an audible taunt, and Lee rose to the bait without a second thought.

'Why? Doesn't the pursuit of such an ordinary occupation have your approval?'

Marc surveyed her in silence, his expression impossible to discern, then his lips moved to form a smile as Alicia rushed in with the information that attaining Cordon Bleu standard could scarcely be considered *ordinary*.

'It would seem the man courageous enough to marry you will be well fed, among other things,' he drawled, taking time to sip wine from his glass. 'Tell me, do you sew a fine seam as well?'

'With reasonable adequacy, yes,' Lee snapped, hating him at that moment with such a depth of emotion that she felt frightened by it.

'Perhaps I'd better warn my bachelor friends,' he smiled with infuriating humour. 'You're a positive threat to their carefree existence.'

'I can't think why,' she advanced coolly, meeting his musing regard with icy disdain. 'I'm quite content with my life the way it is, and I can't envisage any advantage in giving it up in favour of marriage.' There, make of that what you will, she decided silently.

'The epitome of this era's self-sufficient young woman,' he commented idly. '*Brava!* I can almost hear the echoing cheers of your sister-feminists.'

'How typically, boorishly male! The double standard rears its contradictory head once again.' She tilted her head slightly, her fine hazel eyes becoming a fiery gold. 'You've obviously chosen to lead a single life,' she advanced with seeming reason, although there was

no doubt among the others present at the table that
the sparks of war between the indomitable dark-
haired man and the wilful attractive girl seated opposite him were smouldering beneath the surface.
'Since you're almost middle-aged,' she continued
sweetly, enjoying the barb, 'it's unlikely you'll permit
yourself to be trapped into legal bondage.' As a throw-
away line, she concluded, 'I don't imagine you find it
necessary to seek marriage for your—er—physical
needs.'

Marc's subdued laughter brought an angry flush to
her cheeks, and the knowledge that she had allowed a
clash of personalities to reduce her usual good manners to something less than acceptable was galling. It
was hardly desirable dinner table conversation, and
she was furious with herself not to have exercised
restraint.

'Dessert?'

Lee glanced towards Mrs Brascetti with undisguised
relief, and the moment passed.

It wasn't forgotten, for the following morning Alicia
took Lee to task in no uncertain manner the moment
Stefano had left the house and the boys were occupied
after breakfast.

After bearing with an accusatory tirade for more
than ten minutes, Lee threw her hands high in a gesture of defeat. 'Okay—I'm sorry. Honestly,' she
added, glimpsing her sister's distress, 'I don't know
what came over me. Whenever I'm in that hateful
man's company, I seem to change into a snapping little
bitch that's the complete antithesis of the person I
know myself to be.' She glanced over at Alicia with a
faintly puzzled frown. 'He really rubs me the wrong
way.'

'Could it be that you like him subconsciously, and the anger is directed at yourself because you feel he's a threat to your carefree existence?'

'Are you mad?' Lee demanded, and Alicia gave a slight gurgling laugh, a gleam of comprehension lighting her eyes.

'I've been there before, remember?'

'Just what do you mean by that, for heaven's sake?'

Alicia's eyes danced. 'Stefano didn't exactly appeal to me at first, either. In fact,' she added with a laugh, 'I was quite positive I hated him.'

'You are mad,' Lee decided with heavy irony.

'We'll see.'

'Just for that I won't offer to cook dinner tonight,' Lee announced, and caught her sister's expression of mock-dismay. 'I intended making something exotic,' she continued teasingly. 'French,' she deliberated. '*Poulet au riz au safran* for the main course, *marquise à l'ananas* for dessert, and a clear soup to start, I thought.'

'Don't!' Alicia groaned. 'I'm almost prepared to go down on my bended knees.'

Lee broke into uninhibited laugher. 'We can't have that. Mind you,' she added with an attempt at fierceness, 'I'm only cooking because I like preparing food—not for any other reason.'

'Of course not,' her sister sparkled. 'Now, let's check through the ingredients you need. We may have to go into town.'

'I'll make some bread, too,' Lee ruminated, opening and shutting cupboards as she checked their contents against the mental list flashing through her brain. 'Wine—have you got any dry white? And kirsch?'

'Wine, yes. No kirsch,' Alicia told her, and Lee shot her a warm grin.

'Okay, what's the plan of action? Shall I borrow the station wagon and go into town, or do you want to escape while I mind the tribe—or shall we bundle them into the wagon and all go?'

'All,' Alicia decided without hesitation. 'Besides, with you along, it won't be so hectic, and I need a few things that won't wait until Friday.'

Thus followed an action-packed hour and a half, and they returned to the farm with barely sufficient time to prepare lunch, which of necessity comprised grilled steaks and salad followed by fresh fruit.

Immediately after the dishes were dispensed with, Lee began preparations for the evening meal. Spurning Alicia's help, she set about with painstaking care, deriving real enjoyment from the simple domestic tasks. Perhaps it had something to do with possessing an artistic bent, she mused silently well into the afternoon—or perhaps she should have chosen to be a *chef de cuisine* instead of hair stylist.

Engrossed in cutting the pineapples for dessert, Lee didn't hear a vehicle drive into the yard, and it wasn't until Alicia's voice mingled with that of another, deeper and definitely male, reached her ears as they entered the large kitchen that she glanced up and saw Marc Leone's tall frame towering beside her sister.

'Well, well—how nice to see such a scene of domesticity,' Marc drawled as he strolled across the vinyl-covered floor to where she stood.

'Did you think I was fabricating when I admitted I could cook?' Lee questioned defensively. Attired in shorts and a sleeveless working shirt that exposed strong muscular arms, he emanated a raw vibrancy that had every nerve-end rise quivering to the surface,

and the fact that he could affect her so easily made her
angry.

His eyes were openly challenging, their deep grey
depths alive with a devilish humour as his nostrils
flared in deference to the delicious aroma filling the
air.

'No one standing within a hundred yards of this kitchen could doubt your ability,' he commented mildly,
and Lee sensed what could follow even before the
words left Alicia's mouth.

'Come to dinner, Marc,' Alicia insisted, and at that
moment Lee could have cheerfully strangled her.

'I thought you'd never ask,' Marc drawled sardonically, his piercing gaze fixed on Lee's expressive
features. 'I'll bring the wine. Red or white?'

'White,' Lee said distantly, endeavouring to direct
all her attention to the task at hand. Kneading the
dough for the long bread sticks gave her a certain
satisfaction, for she related her irritation with Marc to
the dough, employing rather more vigour than was
strictly necessary.

A brief wail penetrated the air, followed by another,
loud and insistent, and with a rueful grin Alicia
excused herself and disappeared to attend to her
youngest son.

Lee almost jumped out of her skin as a finger
brushed down her cheek, and she threw Marc an
angry glance that would have withered a lesser man.

'Flour,' he mocked, his mouth twisting into a cynical smile as she studiously ignored him. 'My dear
Lee,' he began softly, 'if my presence at dinner is
going to annoy you so much, I'll conveniently remember a prior engagement and stay away.'

'Really?' she shot, her tone heavily sarcastic. 'I

thought you'd come just for the sheer hell of it.'

An eyebrow rose in quizzical appraisal. 'Have you no pity for a bachelor with nothing more appetising planned for dinner than steak and salad which he must prepare himself?'

'My heart bleeds!'

'Callous little wench, aren't you?'

Her smile was a dazzling mockery. 'I'm kind to young children and little old ladies,' she ventured sweetly.

'I was right,' Marc divulged ruminatively. 'You do need taking in hand.'

'By you? Never!'

His husky chuckle was almost her undoing. 'Don't be so sure,' he taunted quietly, and it took all her control to refrain from wrapping the long roll of kneaded dough round his neck.

Alicia's return with baby James settled comfortably against one hip brought the barbed exchange to a halt.

'One angry young man—hungry, wet and alone,' Alicia smiled, her glance flicking quickly from Marc to her sister, and sensing an atmosphere she deposited James into his high chair with a rusk, then extracted juice from the refrigerator and poured some into a spillproof mug. 'There, angel, that will keep you occupied for a few minutes. It's almost time for smoko,' she turned to Marc, her expression faintly pleading. 'Will you stay?'

He softened his refusal with a smile. 'Thanks, Alicia, but I must get back.' He turned and playfully tickled James' chin, and was rewarded with a gurgling laugh, then with a sketchy salute he moved out the door. Seconds later the car door slammed and the engine sprang to life, its muted roar fading rapidly in the distance.

'What were you and Marc talking about?'

Lee set the long measured lengths of dough on to a tray and placed them in the oven, then straightening, she moved back to the bench. 'I was adding my invitation to yours in persuading Marc to stay for dinner,' she invented, not wishing to invoke a lecture by revealing the truth of their exchange, and to her relief Alicia appeared to accept it at face value.

The remainder of the afternoon passed in a whirl of flurried activity, and scarcely before Lee realised it was time to change and freshen up prior to Marc Leone's arrival. A hurried shower followed by a few minutes' deliberation over what she would wear had her reaching for a cream linen dress whose neat tailored lines bore an understated simplicity. Shunning any use of make-up, she brushed her hair until it shone, its length flowing freely about her shoulders, then she hastily smoothed a touch of moisturiser over her face and rubbed the excess into her hands. Slipping her feet into low-heeled backless sandals, she emerged from her room and made her way towards the kitchen.

The boys had been fed over an hour ago, and baby James was already asleep—although for how long was debatable, Alicia announced as she put the finishing touches to the long dining table.

'Poor little mite—it is his teeth?' Lee enquired, and she received an affirmative nod.

'Stefano is almost ready,' her sister informed her, then slanting her head she announced, 'There's a car now. It must be Marc.'

Lee felt her stomach give an unexpected lurch, and

the few minutes it took for Marc to enter the house were sufficient for her to regain her composure. Dressed in casual trousers and an open-necked shirt, he exuded a powerful, raw-boned force she found difficult to handle, and the greeting she extended was cool and faintly aloof.

'The wine,' Marc drawled, placing two bottles down onto the counter, and his eyes were vaguely mocking as he allowed his gaze to rove unhurriedly over her. 'It's a recommended vintage which I trust will meet with your approval.'

Lee removed each from their wrapping, inspected the labels, and inclined her head. 'Thank you.'

Stefano joined them and the tension lessened, much to Lee's relief, and she shooed Alicia out of the kitchen to join the men in the lounge for a drink. 'Go *on*,' she urged, sensing her sister's reluctance. 'I'll be there in a few minutes.' Unfortunately, she added silently, not really looking forward to the verbal fencing she knew to be ahead of her. Each encounter with Marc Leone seemed to endorse the private war between them, and it angered her unbearably that he regarded her feministic ideals with such undisguised mockery.

After five minutes of unnecessary checking Lee drew a deep breath and moved through the dining-room towards the lounge. There was no valid reason to delay joining the others any longer, and if she waited too long it would only lend credence to Marc's suspicions that she would rather not join them at all. She was darned if she would give him that satisfaction!

Consequently when she entered the lounge there was the faint light of battle evident in her eyes, and the rigid set of her slim shoulders served to emphasise her mood.

'Lee,' Stefano greeted affectionately. 'What will you

have? Sherry, or something stronger?'

She needed something to steady her ragged nerves. 'A light sherry will be fine,' she indicated, moving towards her sister, and she accepted the slim fluted glass Stefano handed her, sipping the contents carefully, her attention centred on Marc's broad chest. She didn't want to lift her gaze higher, and for the umpteenth time she silently cursed Alicia for inviting him to dinner.

Conscious of the electric atmosphere, Stefano made reference to the seed-beds, elicited when Marc intended to plant out, and with Alicia's help ensured that the conversation didn't develop a lull. Lee's contribution was desultory, and it was all she could do not to give an outward sigh of relief when ten minutes later she excused herself to dish out the soup.

The meal was a gastronomic delight, although Lee hardly tasted any of the food she put in her mouth. As each course was dispensed with, Alicia evinced words in praise until Lee thought she must surely scream. It all seemed so contrived, as if the entire evening had been deliberately set up to show her in a good light to their guest.

'That was delicious,' Marc praised, sliding his dessert plate aside, and Lee sent him a polite smile that nowhere near reached her eyes. 'You must allow me to take you out to dinner. Such an excellent meal deserves some recompense.'

Oh lord, how did she get out of this one? 'Thank you,' she acknowledged, adding with sudden inspiration, 'Unfortunately my tastes run to French cuisine, and I wouldn't presume to suggest the long drive down to Cairns.'

'There's a very good restaurant in Atherton,' Marc

informed her with mockery. 'A little unusual for a small country town, but the food is definitely Provençal. I've frequented it on numerous occasions, and haven't been able to fault it. Shall we say tomorrow night?'

'What a lovely idea,' Alicia enthused, her expression assuming open delight, and Lee experienced total exasperation as she glanced towards the dark-haired man whose saturnine features were deliberately bland.

'Alicia will tell you that I often cook a meal whenever I'm here on vacation. It's a hobby I enjoy indulging, and besides, it gives my sister a rest.' She summoned a smile. 'It's thoughtful of you to suggest it, but quite unnecessary,' she concluded evenly.

'I'll be offended if you refuse,' he said with quizzical amusement, and she had to forcibly refrain from flinging the salt-shaker at him.

'In that case, I shall have to accept, shan't I?'

His eyes gleamed as he said softly, 'I'm not accustomed to accepting a refusal.'

Lee clenched her fists under cover of the table, not trusting herself to speak, and Stefano reached for the wine, refilling first Marc's glass, then his own.

Almost at the end of her patience, Lee was about to begin collecting the plates together with the intention of taking them through to the kitchen when a thin wail rose from one of the boys' bedrooms, and clutching at the excuse to leave the dining-room, she rose to her feet, declaring that she would see what ailed her youngest nephew.

Her relief at escaping was evident in her expressive features, and she scooped up the tear-soaked squalling bundle with a conciliatory murmur, watching in between nuzzling his warm sweet-smelling neck as the sobs came to a hiccuping halt and a damp bubbly smile creased his face.

'Poor little man,' she soothed. 'I bet you're wet, and have a sore mouth, to boot.' She laid him gently down on to the bed and reached for a dry towelling square. 'We'll attend to one end, then deal with the other, hm?' She blew him a kiss, followed by several more as she changed him, then she collected him in her arms and carried him out to the kitchen. His tiny arms stole round her neck and he nestled his head against the curve of her throat. 'Poor sweetheart, aren't you?' she murmured, reaching out to open the cupboard in which Alicia kept the children's medicine. 'We'll take this in to Mum, I think. She's had more practice.'

Lee turned and came face to face with Marc, who regarded her thoughtfully for several seconds before remarking with indolent amusement,

'Right at this moment, you look far removed from the career-girl image you try so hard to project.'

'You are the most hateful, egotistical man I've ever met!' Lee hissed wrathfully, becoming utterly incensed as he slowly shook his head from side to side.

'You'd better consign that young man to me,' Marc declared, moving to extricate James from her arms, 'before he senses his beloved aunt is other than the gentle female he knows her to be.'

'I hope he throws up all over you!'

Marc gave a careless shrug as he settled the child into the curve of his arm. 'It wouldn't be the first time. I have a few nieces and a nephew of my own.'

'You surprise me,' Lee threw with quiet vehemence. 'You don't look the type to play with the *young*.'

His look was openly sardonic. 'Remind me to spank you some time.'

Her scandalous response had of necessity to be curtailed as Alicia entered the kitchen, and with a muttered excuse Lee turned and almost ran to the dining-room on the pretext of clearing the table.

The chore of washing and drying dishes provided a necessary respite from Marc's hateful presence, and afterwards when the coffee was made and Lee took the tray into the lounge she couldn't recall one solitary item of conversation with her sister, such was her pre-occupation with their guest.

The mere sight of him was enough to revive bitter memory of his mouth and the utter devastation it could wreak. Those tanned hands, broad-palmed, their fingers possessing a strength and tactile sensuousness that was frightening. There wasn't a thing he didn't know about women. It was there in his eyes, an indolent cynicism combined with an indomitable will—and she shivered in the knowledge that if he chose to pursue his quarry, it would be to the death with no doubt over who would emerge the victor. Like a jungle cat, there was latent savagery in every muscle and sinew, and in that moment she wanted to pack her few clothes and board the first flight back to Sydney, and safety.

CHAPTER FOUR

'LEE, you're not wearing that, are you?' Alicia demanded in strangled tones, her face creasing with incredulity, and Lee hid a satisfied smile.

If her outfit had this effect on Alicia, just think what

it was going to do to Marc! Reaching out her hands, she made a slow twirl, then came to a halt, one eyebrow raised in mocking enquiry. 'It's the latest fashion down south,' she explained with a shrug. 'Go to any disco and you'll see every second girl is wearing just this.'

'This' was hip-hugging long trousers in pale silver satin stretch material, high-heeled backless sandals, a body-hugging strapless shirred top in matching satin over which she wore a blouson-styled blouse in floral transparent chiffon. Her make-up was skilfully applied, the eyeshadow and mascara bold, the blusher highlighting delicate cheekbones, and lip-gloss over rich garnet red gave her mouth a seductive provocativeness.

'Mareeba—or rather, Atherton,' Alicia corrected wryly, 'isn't "down south". Not only will you shock the natives, you'll probably create a riot.'

'And Marc wouldn't approve?'

'My dear Lee,' her sister began dryly, 'you look gorgeous and very—sexy, a turn-on for any red-blooded male. Are you sure you can handle the inevitable reaction?'

'Ah, but I'll have my protector at my side,' Lee advanced with a trace of cynicism, and Alicia gave an unladylike snort.

'If you're up to anything—and I think you are—be careful,' she warned. 'Marc isn't your usual run-of-the-mill man to play careless games with. I may be your sister, married, with three children and another on the way, but I'm still woman enough to recognise a macho male when I see one,' she added musingly, and Lee gave a grimace of distaste.

'Macho—the word is overrated, and used to the

point of nausea. Pick up any film magazine and you'll
see every male star under fifty so described.'

Alicia's eyes twinkled with irrepressible humour.
'Each to their own opinion—but in my book, Marc is
one very macho male!'

Lee pulled a face, and opening a small clutch purse
she conducted a quick inspection of its contents, then
satisfied, she moved back towards her bedroom.

'Hey, where are you going? Marc will be here any
minute.'

'He can wait,' Lee declared uncharitably. 'Five
minutes won't hurt him.'

'But you're ready!' Alicia wailed, and Lee gave an
unabashed grin.

'I know that, and so do you. But I'm not eager for
this wretched dinner date, and I'm darned if I'll
appear ready and willing by hovering on the doorstep
waiting for his lordship's arrival!'

Alicia shook her head. 'You're playing with fire,
Lee, if you think you can get the better of Marc.'

Lee's answering shrug reflected her negligent atti-
tude, and with a faint smile she turned back and
walked down the hall.

Almost as soon as she reached her room she heard a
car door slam, then seconds later the sound of a deep
male voice greeting Alicia.

The minutes ticked by as she leafed idly through a
magazine, then when she judged sufficient time had
passed she stood to her feet and took a final cursory
glance at her appearance in the mirror.

Lee's entrance into the lounge lacked the impact she
expected, for Marc simply turned from speaking with
Stefano and greeted her with amused politeness.

Elegantly attired in light grey trousers, a matching

jacket beneath which he wore a navy shirt, he bore the air of a successful man whose sophistication seemed slightly out of focus with farm life.

Alicia covered Lee's lack of conversation with some innocuous anecdotes concerning the children, and although Marc had very little remaining of his drink, Lee accepted Stefano's offer of a sherry, thanked him charmingly when he handed her the glass, and deliberately took her time consuming its contents.

Unable to delay their departure any longer, Lee preceded Marc out to the car, and safely seated she surreptitiously watched him move round the vehicle and slip in behind the wheel.

A sketchy wave to her sister and brother-in-law, then the large car was moving out of sight past the farm buildings on to the road, and as it picked up speed Lee experienced a momentary feeling of apprehension. With it came the sure knowledge that she must be mad to be accompanying Marc on a dinner date—or anywhere, for that matter. Yet she could hardly ask him to turn the car round and take her home. But this was the last time—positively the *last* time she would consent to go out with him. Admittedly she would have to resign herself to seeing him again, often, if she was to fit in with the arrangements Alicia and Stefano had made for her enjoyment. Any further invitations from Marc Leone would be met with a firm, and if necessary, rude refusal!

'You're very quiet.'

Lee spared the man seated beside her a swift analytical glance. 'I'm sorry,' she began without any hint of regret. 'I didn't realise you required me to provide idle chit-chat. Perhaps you can suggest something we can discuss in amicable accord that won't digress into a heated argument?' she concluded sweetly, and coloured a delicate pink at his husky laughter.

'I've no desire to tangle with you so early in the evening,' Marc revealed mockingly. 'By all means be silent—it will give me time to prepare myself for an inevitable verbal battle.' He leaned forward and switched on the car radio, then he set the vehicle speeding along the bitumen until they approached Mareeba township.

Several cars lined the streets, and the hotels showed evidence of being well patronised. Past the township's restricted limit the car picked up speed and maintained it beneath Marc's competent hands. Darkness had fallen and there was little to be seen beyond the powerful beam of the headlights, although as they drove further inland the temperature appeared to cool slightly.

Atherton was a small town centred amidst a rural community whose main agricultural interests were cattle and peanut farming. A French restaurant in such a setting was an unlikely but rewarding bonus, for after a quick look at the menu Lee cautiously decided it was possible it just might live up to its expectations.

Marc was accorded a certain deference by the staff, and the service given them couldn't be faulted. Apart from enquiring her choice, he made no effort to converse, and after the first course had been dispensed with Lee began to feel the small measure of self-confidence she retained melt into insignificance with every passing minute.

'Are you playing tit-for-tat?' she enquired lightly, and caught the faint twitch of his lips as he regarded her.

'Whatever gives you that idea?'

'You haven't said a word since we left Mareeba,' she said dryly, meeting his thoughtful gaze a shade defiantly.

'As you made it plain you didn't intend to talk, there hardly seemed any point in me making the effort.'

'I see.'

'Do you, Lee?' he drawled.

'Look,' she began angrily, 'if you've invited me out simply because of your friendship with my brother-in-law—don't bother again.'

An eyebrow rose in quizzical appraisal. 'Is that what you think?'

'We don't like each other, so it's certainly not due to a mutual empathy!'

Marc's gleaming gaze assumed wicked amusement. 'Oh, Lee,' he taunted softly, 'how can you say that?' Even white teeth showed as his lips parted in a cynical smile. 'I retain a vivid memory of one thing in which we appear to be in perfect accord.'

She felt her cheeks tinge a heated red, and leaned forward, indignation evident in every pore. 'A kiss taken with brutal force? My God——'

'It may have started out that way,' he drawled imperturbably, and she retaliated with barely subdued fury,

'I bow down to your undoubted expertise, but I was in no danger of losing my head!'

His gaze was direct and needle-sharp. 'I didn't allow you to do so.'

Lee was speechless, a mixture of emotions flickered over her mobile features, and it was perhaps as well that at that moment their main course was brought to the table.

'Some more wine?' Marc enquired smoothly, and at her terse nod he filled her near-empty glass.

Chicken in breadcrumbs braised in garlic butter set up an appetising aroma which Lee found impossible to resist, and ignoring Marc completely she began doing justice to the plate set before her.

The restaurant was small, its setting intimate, with candles at each table and the main lighting subdued. Off the main street, it existed by reputation alone, and for a week night it was well patronised. There was even a space set aside for dancing, and Lee became aware that a small band was responsible for the background music.

With an inward sigh of satisfaction Lee placed her cutlery down on to her plate and pushed it slightly to one side. The dressing on the assorted salad greens had had an expert's touch, and she would have given much to discover the chef's recipe. She stretched out an idle hand and lifted the wineglass to her lips, sipping the excellent Moselle with true appreciation.

'Dare I suggest we dance?'

Lee glanced across the table and met Marc's enigmatic gaze. 'Why not?' Setting her glass down on the table, she stood to her feet and allowed him to lead her towards the dance floor.

She hadn't bargained for the way her traitorous body would respond to being held close to his muscular frame, and she felt her pulse quicken despite a resolution to remain impassive.

The music lilted slowly around the room, its mood conventional and designed no doubt to aid rather than impair digestion. Later it would probably become more lively, but the muted rendition was soothing, and Lee felt some of the tension leave as Marc moved with flawless timing. His touch was hardly impersonal, but she felt disinclined to move out of his grasp as they slowly circled the small square.

Her eyes were level with the strong tanned column of his throat, and with a small sigh she let her hands slowly climb towards his shoulders, then move to clasp together around his neck. She could feel his chin brush against the top of her hair—or was it his lips? And somehow she was enfolded very close against him. Too close, she realised minutes later, and moved slightly away from his muscular length, unable to still a faint flush of embarrassment.

'Shocked?' Marc queried with a certain wryness as he raked her expressive features.

Lee contrived a nonchalant shrug, but didn't quite manage it.

'You're a very desirable young woman,' he told her sardonically. 'Surely you haven't reached the age of twenty-two without being made aware of it?'

After a few seconds Lee found her voice. 'Of course not,' she acknowledged coolly, lifting her gaze to meet those dark depths unflinchingly.

His eyes never left hers, and in the end it was she who had to glance away.

'Oh, Lee,' Marc mocked softly. 'You're quite safe—you have my word.'

'I've heard that one before,' Lee declared dryly.

'You don't trust me?' The words were quietly delivered, but nonetheless she couldn't control the shiver of apprehension that feathered an icy trail down her spine.

'I hardly know you,' she offered, and he regarded her musingly.

'We can easily rectify that.'

Lee's chin tilted. 'With what object in mind? I don't go in for holiday——' she paused, then elucidated with delicacy—'romps.' Her eyes were a clear brilliant topaz. 'Besides, we seem to strike sparks off each other at every turn.'

His eyes gleamed with hidden laughter. 'So you do admit we generate a certain body chemistry?'

'What does that prove?' she parried lightly, and caught his cynical amusement.

'Do you want me to show you?'

The thought of just how easily she had succumbed to the magnetic power of his kiss only a few days previously was enough to strengthen her resolve to put as much distance between them as possible. 'Please, I'd like to go back to our table.' She moved out of his arms and preceded him across the floor, and when she was seated she reached for her glass, disposing of its contents with scant regard for its potency.

Dessert was served, and Lee transferred the delectable fruit salad into her mouth without tasting a solitary thing. As the silence stretched between them, she searched desperately for something to say.

'Do you often travel abroad?'

Marc glanced across the table, his expression faintly cynical. 'Yes. Not always on business, and rarely alone.'

'Naturally.'

'Jealous?'

Lee gave an indignant gasp. 'Why should I be? You're the last man I'd consider as a——'

'Lover?' he inserted deliberately, and she clenched her hands in anger.

'Yes, damn you!' She looked at him with impotent

fury, then effected a grimace of distaste. 'Oh, for heaven's sake, let's end this farcical evening. We haven't a civil word to say to each other!'

'No,' Marc agreed blandly. 'We do much better when we don't talk at all.'

'You're impossible, do you know that?' she demanded, and was incensed when she heard his husky laughter. 'I want to go home.'

'Simmer down, Lee. We're about to be invaded by a few friends of mine,' he told her sardonically, returning his glance from its sweeping appraisal of the room.

Lee found it difficult to control her features into something resembling politeness as a man and two young women joined them.

Marc effected the introductions with ease. 'Daniella, Marita, and John Conti—Lee Carruthers.'

'When did you get back? It's seemed ages since we last saw each other,' Daniella declared with a pretty pout. Dark-haired with luminous brown eyes, she was utterly gorgeous, and had a figure and personality to match. It was also patently obvious that she regarded Marc in an intimate light.

Lee cast a surreptitious glance at Marita, and saw that she too was eyeing Marc with open adoration. The likeness between the two girls was startling, so much so that Lee could only conclude they were sisters.

'Have you eaten?' Marc queried smoothly. 'Perhaps you'd care to join us?'

'We've been here for ten minutes,' Marita declared, and her expressive features creased in puzzlement. 'How is it possible we didn't see you?'

Marc's smile held faint mockery. 'Possibly because you didn't look?'

'You should have come over to our table,' Daniella remonstrated gently, and Marc merely smiled.

'I'll order some more wine,' he said, and Lee was aware of the close scrutiny she received. It was clear her presence was resented, and she sensed the two sisters were assessing her as a possible threat to their chances with Marc.

The idea seemed so ludicrous she had to suppress the laugh that bubbled in her throat. Her eyes slid towards Marc, and as if he sensed her amusement he directed a slow warm smile that made her blink. The intended intimacy was evident to everyone present, and Lee could almost feel the united force of Daniella and Marita's anger. If Marc had deliberately placed a cat among the pigeons, he couldn't have achieved a more successful result, she perceived wryly.

'Did your mother enjoy the trip?' John queried lightly. It was obvious he was aware of the electric atmosphere his sisters were creating, and from the expression of amused resignation on his pleasant features it clearly wasn't the first time Daniella and Marita had vied for Marc's attention.

Lee's hazel depths deepened to a sparkling bronze as she swung to face him, and the faintly cynical lift of her eyebrows brought forth a mocking twist from his mouth. *Mother?*

'Immensely,' he answered amiably, and Daniella leaned towards him, extending a softened smile.

'Did she come north with you, Marc?'

'She preferred to spend some time with my sister after being away for several months. I'm expecting her next week.'

Lee found it difficult to hide her amazement, and despite her efforts it must have shown, for Marc directed her a sardonic smile.

'Everyone has a mother—even me,' he taunted, and Lee gave a helpless shrug.

'You never mentioned her,' she murmured, and heard Daniella's sharp laugh.

'Good heavens, Marc's mother is a devoted *mamma*. She spends the winter up north with Marc, and the summer in Sydney with Angelina. I thought you would have known that.'

Lee cast her a cool glance. 'I only met Marc a few days ago,' she said evenly, and to her utter consternation Marc reached out and caught her hand in his, holding it fast in a grip that was vaguely cruel.

'We've been so preoccupied with each other, the subject of my family never arose,' he declared, and his eyes dared her to struggle and create a scene.

John's laughter was genuine, but the looks Lee received from his sisters held bitter enmity, and suddenly Lee felt sickened at the way Marc was deliberately playing her against the other two girls.

'If you'll excuse me,' she declared, firmly extricating her hand. With a polite smile she stood to her feet and made for the powder room. Anything to get away from the animosity that hung like a shroud over the table.

It was almost ten minutes before Lee returned, and the sight of Daniella closely wrapped in Marc's arms on the dance floor hit her like a physical pain so that for an infinitesimal moment she was devoid of breath.

Oh dear God—*no*! It wasn't possible she was jealous—was it? Marc Leone was the antithesis of everything she admired in a man. He was neither gentle nor kind, and he possessed an indomitable strength that she found totally unconscionable. Besides, she hated him to a point whereby she could hardly offer a civil word in his presence.

Almost as soon as Lee reached their table, John rose to his feet and asked her to dance, and she accepted, directing him such a stunning smile he almost reeled from its effect.

'Are you Marc's exclusive property?'

Lee glanced at him with ill-concealed mockery. 'Why, John, whatever gives you that idea?'

'I don't want to poach on his preserves.'

'You're not,' she declared with succinct sarcasm, and he lifted an enquiring eyebrow.

'So definite?'

Lee gave a light laugh and slipped into his arms. 'I'm my own woman, John. No one has a prior claim on me.'

His eyes gleamed appreciatively. 'I'm glad. How about coming out with me tomorrow night?'

'Could you ring me?' she suggested. 'I'm staying with my sister and brother-in-law—Alicia and Stefano Brascetti. You know them, I presume?'

'Of course. Are you on holiday?'

Her answer was a monosyllabic averral, and John gave an eloquent sigh. 'Just my luck! And to compound it, I suppose you're returning home soon.'

Lee's mouth dimpled. 'I've another two weeks yet.'

'Well, now you're talking,' he enthused. 'A lot can happen in two weeks.'

When the music paused for the band to take a break, Lee moved back towards their table with John, and a devilish imp prompted her to flirt a little.

Marc was already seated, flanked on either side by Daniella and Marita, who were giving him more attention than any one man deserved, Lee decided as she slipped into the chair John held out for her.

'I'll order more wine,' said John, shooting a glance at his watch. 'The bar is due to close soon.'

While he was gone Lee met and matched Marc's enigmatic appraisal, her smile a brilliant facsimile of her apparent enjoyment. A gleam of sudden anger flared in those dark grey depths, and try as she might she couldn't glance away.

He had no right to look at her like that, Lee perceived some minutes later when a few sips of wine had restored her composure. But the damage was done, and when John asked her to dance as soon as the music began again she accepted with alacrity.

'Poor Marc,' John accorded with a grin. 'First Daniella, and now Marita.'

Lee made a slight grimace. 'Why "poor" Marc?' she demanded. 'Two beautiful girls, each vying for his attention. The man must be in his element!'

'My dear Lee,' he commented musingly, 'despite the fact they're my sisters, those two girls are positive man-eaters. Especially where Marc is concerned. They've been fighting over him since they were in their early teens!'

'How—awkward, for him,' Lee said wryly, and incurred John's mirth.

'Oh, Lee! Marc can take care of himself. He's managed to elude more women than I care to count.'

'Really?' she queried with contrived disinterest. Determined to change the subject, she enquired, 'Do you live in Atherton? Or do you grow tobacco?'

'Tobacco. Our farm is several miles away from that of Marc's—the other side of Dimbulah, in fact. However, it isn't anywhere near as well established, nor as productive.'

'I've only visited during the off-season,' Lee began,

sparing him an interested glance. 'But I believe cultivating and curing the crop is hard work, and not for the faint of heart.'

'It's a piece of cake now, compared to what it was fifteen years ago,' John related seriously. 'Mechanisation, sophisticated poisons, have almost eliminated the necessity for outside manual labour. When I was a teenager, there were upwards of eight men working through the season. Depending on the acreage being grown, that number could rise to twelve men working a ten-hour day, six days a week. My mother had to cook huge meals and provide smokos morning and afternoon. As well as that, she strung tobacco to go into the barns, and upon completion of the picking season she would grade the cured leaves. It was hard work,' he elaborated. 'Long arduous hours in the heat of summer.'

Lee gave a shudder at the grim picture he painted. 'I guess I'm city-orientated,' she smiled, and he slanted her a musing grin.

'Tied to an office desk, nine to five?' he hazarded, and she laughingly shook her head.

'No,' she denied. 'Standing on my feet all day tending to women's hair—and men's. It's an exacting occupation.'

'From which you've won temporary reprieve. I hope you'll permit me to provide some light entertainment,' he said seriously, and she gave a non-committal,

'Occasionally, perhaps. Although I owe first priority to Alicia and my small nephews,' she added. 'They're the only family I have.'

The music took an upward swing, emulating the latest pop discs, and with a laugh Lee stepped back a pace and began moving her body in time to the beat. Out of the corner of her eye she saw Marc and Marita follow suit. Daniella was on the floor, too, with a young man who at first glance seemed much too tame for John's volatile sister.

Eventually there came a break, and back at their table Marc ordered coffee, declaring a need to curtail the evening.

'I have a full day ahead of me tomorrow,' he explained, tempering it with a smile as both Daniella and Marita endeavoured to dissuade him from leaving.

'When will we see you again?' Daniella cajoled a trifle petulantly, and he gave an enigmatic shrug.

'At Francesca's wedding on Saturday, I presume.'

'Come to dinner on Sunday,' Marita begged. 'Mum and Dad were only asking about you the other day. They'd adore to hear about your trip.'

'Thank you,' Marc slanted equably. 'I'll let you know.' He glanced across the table and met Lee's faintly cynical smile. 'If you've finished your coffee, we'll get away.'

As Lee rose to her feet, John leaned forward and said in an audible undertone,

'I'll ring you tomorrow, around midday.'

In the car Lee sank back against the cushioned seat, and within minutes they had reached the outskirts of Atherton. The dark of night was lightened by the moon's opalescent glow, bathing the surrounding terrain in a milky half-light that had a curious stilling effect.

'You seem to have scored a hit with John,' Marc observed sardonically, and Lee returned sweetly,

'As you did with his sisters.'

His husky laughter was galling. 'Should I apologise

for their intrusion?'

'Good heavens,' she feigned incredulity without the slightest difficulty, assuring him, 'I welcomed it. Their presence provided some light relief.'

'From me?'

'You guessed it.'

'Pity,' he slanted mockingly. 'Especially as you're fated to spend another evening in my company tomorrow night.'

'Sorry,' she refused disparagingly, 'John beat you to it.'

'When he phones, you'll tell him you have a prior engagement.'

'The hell I will,' Lee declared emphatically. Just who did he think he was?

The look he threw her was startlingly level. 'Didn't Alicia tell you about the arrangements for tomorrow evening?'

'What arrangements are those?' she demanded angrily. 'Something you've concocted, no doubt!'

'Alicia, Stefano and you are my guests for the evening. I've made reservations at a restaurant in Cairns,' Marc informed her brusquely, his eyes on the straight stretch of road ahead. 'Stefano's parents are having the children overnight.'

'If that's true, why didn't she tell me?'

'Probably because it slipped her mind.'

Lee turned slightly to face him, her features stormy. 'Tell me something—do you always get your own way?'

His reply was silky-smooth, and for some reason it set the butterflies in her stomach fluttering madly. 'If by that, you mean I go all out for my objective—then the answer is yes.'

'Which in this case, is *what*, precisely?'

'Are you really that naïve?'

Lee's face burned, and she stared straight ahead, not deigning to offer another word. Everything she had ever recalled to describe him tumbled to her lips longing to find a voice, and it required every ounce of effort not to lash out and physically strike him.

It took thirty minutes to reach Mareeba, and a further five to the turn-off leading to the Brascetti farm, and those minutes seemed the longest Lee had ever spent. As the car slowed and veered off the main road she experienced a feeling of faint relief that within a few minutes she would be out of Marc's dynamic presence.

Lee reached for the door clasp the instant they drew to a halt in the gravelled yard, only to have her flight forestalled as a hand grasped her arm.

'In such a hurry?' Marc drawled, and she turned back in fury.

'To get away from you—*yes*!'

'Afraid, Lee?' he demanded with smiling mockery, and she let out an angry gasp.

'What is it you want, Marc? A goodnight kiss in return for providing an evening's entertainment?' Even the thought of those sensuous lips taking possession of her own was enough to make her limbs become weak and jelly-like, and unconsciously her voice became husky. 'Or do you have something more——' she paused, and he finished smoothly,

'Intimate?' His eyes gleamed with sardonic amusement as he probed lazily, 'Is that what you think?' He gave a soft laugh, and leaning slightly towards her he trailed gentle fingers down her cheek. 'I find you very transparent. In spite of all that brilliant fury, you respond with a passion that both promises and provokes.' Very gently he touched her lips and felt them tremble as he traced their fullness. 'Oh yes, Lee,' he taunted, 'I want you—shockingly.' Slowly his fingers travelled down to her throat and played distractedly with the fine bones before edging downwards. 'With very little effort I could make you want me—almost as much.'

Lee moistened her lips without conscious thought, unaware of the provocativeness of her action, and she gave a soundless gasp as his fingers slid beneath the shirred bodice and cupped one creamy breast, then his mouth was on hers, soft and deliberately tantalising, playing with her lips until of their own volition they parted hungrily to welcome his invasion.

There was no awareness of time, only a floating mindless sensation that made her ache for complete fulfilment, and a return to sanity was wrought as Marc disentangled her arms and gently pushed her away.

'Go inside, Lee. I'll see you tomorrow.' His voice was husky and faintly sardonic as he leaned across and opened her door, and after a second's pause she slid out and almost ran across the grass verge towards the verandah.

The front door was unlatched, and she stepped inside and closed it behind her without so much as a backward glance, and as she moved quietly towards her room she heard the faint noise of a car engine accompanied by the crunching sound of tire-rubber on gravel, then there was nothing, only the stillness of the night.

Lee prepared for bed with the movements of an automaton, and long after she had slipped between the cool crisp sheets she lay staring into the darkness, reliving with agonising clarity the memory of her shameless abandon in his arms. The words—'with very little effort I could make you want me'—echoed and re-echoed damnably inside her brain, until with a tortured sob she buried her head beneath the pillow issuing a fervent prayer that sleep might provide a welcome release.

CHAPTER FIVE

IN spite of Lee's conviction that the evening could only be a disaster, Alicia and Stefano's presence ensured that it was not, and Marc assumed the role of an urbane host, projecting a warm friendliness towards both women, so that Lee could only wonder if the passion they had shared the previous evening had been little more than a figment of her imagination.

The restaurant Marc had chosen specialised in Italian cuisine, and they enjoyed a leisurely three-course meal before ordering coffee. By then it was almost ten o'clock, and mindful of Alicia's condition and the prospect of the wedding the following afternoon and the ensuing reception and dance in the Shire Hall, thus entailing another late night, they decided to embark on the long drive home.

On reflection Lee had to concede that the evening had been an enjoyable one, despite Marc's presence, and her initial wariness had almost disappeared by the time he deposited them home. Quite what she expected when he bade them goodnight she wasn't sure, but his sketched salute that encompassed them all left her feeling vaguely unsettled.

Like all the days preceding it, Saturday dawned bright and clear with nary a cloud in sight, and as Lee entered the large concrete-structured church with Alicia and Stefano she couldn't help the surreptitious glance she cast over the congregation. Among so many people it was difficult to distinguish a familiar head, and she felt unaccountably cross with herself for even bothering to look.

The ceremony was solemn, with the added dignity of a nuptial mass, and it wasn't until the guests had vacated the church that Lee caught sight of Marc and Daniella and Marita standing possessively close either side of him.

Attired in a dark formal suit he was an arresting figure, and Lee felt her heart give an unaccustomed lurch as he turned slightly and met her glance. His faint smile did strange things to her equilibrium, and she returned the smile with one of her own before swinging back to engage Alicia in a bright conversation which had that good woman frowning in perplexity.

The reception was a large affair with countless guests, and much to Lee's discomfiture she found herself seated opposite Marc, who was again flanked by Daniella and Marita. No doubt about it, both girls deserved an 'A' for persistence! By some feat of agility, John had managed to seat himself next to Lee, and throughout the lavish meal and the accompanying speeches and toasts she summoned the necessary will-power to project an image of a guest enjoying the proceedings. Difficult, when all she was aware of was the provocative and positively sickening way Daniella and Marita vied for Marc's attention. On more than one occasion she had to physically restrain herself from splashing the excellent champagne over their smug little faces!

Consequently, when the tables were cleared and dismantled so that the dancing could commence, Lee didn't hesitate when John indicated they should take to the floor.

'You look ravishing.'

Lee cast a swift glance over the simply styled blue silk dress she wore, then lifted sparkling eyes and met his earnest smile. 'Why, thank you, kind sir. You cut a dashing figure yourself.'

'Francesca looks gorgeous, doesn't she? Lucky Tony!'

Lee detected a note of envy, and something more, in his tone. 'Your two sisters are attracting a lot of attention,' she said lightly. 'They're both very beautiful.'

His faint grimace brought forth a questioning glance, and he laughed. 'They're constantly in the throes of a private war—over who will win the inestimable Marc Leone,' he slanted with droll cynicism. 'Our presence in Atherton was no chance happening, my dear Lee. That restaurant is a favourite haunt of Marc's, and knowing that he was back from abroad, it was reasonable to assume he might be there. As older brother, I was persuaded against my better judgment to escort them. Even todays's manoeuvres required careful planning,' he added mockingly. 'You don't imagine it's by chance they managed to sit beside him?' His laugh held amusement as he grinned down at her. 'The man is no fool, and he manages to extricate himself with remarkable agility. I doubt there's a woman alive who could trap him.'

'Bravo for Marc,' Lee accorded wryly, and incurred John's mirth.

'There isn't a woman in this room under the age of forty who doesn't covet him—married or not.'

She contrived a scandalised expression. 'Why, John, are you trying to shock me?'

The look he cast her was wholly serious. 'Are you shockable, Lee?'

'That would depend on what you intended,' she countered evenly, and saw him smile.

'Come to dinner tomorrow night,' he pleaded. 'Daniella and Marita have invited Marc, and I need you to provide a distraction.' His cheeky grin made her laugh.

'Invitation accepted.'

They had only just returned to the edge of the floor when a deep voice drawled,

'Do you mind if I commandeer Lee for a dance?'

She turned to meet Marc's sardonic smile and was on the point of refusing when John acquiesced and moved towards his two sisters, so that she had little choice but to move out on to the floor.

'You could have asked me,' Lee snapped with acerbity, and Marc cast her a penetrating glance.

'And have you refuse?'

'Why me? You appeared to be enjoying marked adulation from two very attractive young girls,' she reasoned sweetly.

'Would you believe it was in the form of duty?'

Her laugh was frankly disbelieving. 'Oh, Marc,' she chided. '*Duty?*'

His voice became droll. 'I'm not unaware of my potential in the marriage stakes. If I dance more than once with the same girl it will be construed that I may be considering putting an end to my bachelor existence,' he elaborated mockingly, and she tilted her head, feigning disbelief.

'The great Marc Leone settling down to matrimony—with *one* woman? Good heavens, who would be fool enough to have you?'

One eyebrow slanted in cynical amusement. 'You don't consider there would be sufficient compensations?'

'Possibly,' Lee allowed with a disinterested shrug, then added, 'In all except one—fidelity. I can't imagine it to be one of your virtues,' she finished dryly.

'A reformed rake?'

'Rake, I agree,' she snorted with derision. 'Reformed? Never!'

'What were you and John discussing?' Marc queried with deceptive mildness, and Lee lifted her head to meet his enigmatic features.

'That's an infringement of privacy,' she opined evenly. 'How would you feel if I asked the same of you and Daniella, or Marita—or any one of the many other young women in whose company you've been this evening?'

His subdued laugh was a husky sound deep in his throat. 'Would you believe fielding several invitations to dinner?'

'How nice to be so popular,' she remarked with pseudo-sweetness.

'And John? The two of you appeared to have a lot to say to each other,' Marc drawled, and her eyes widened slightly.

'I didn't realise we interested you to such an extent,' she remarked innocently. 'Otherwise I would have had John stand directly beside you so that you could have overheard every word.'

Her hand was caught in an excruciating grip. 'Don't

try my patience too far,' Marc threatened softly, and she gave him a stunning smile.

'What can you possibly do to me in front of a room full of people?'

His eyes darkened measurably. 'Are you daring me, Lee?'

'Are you threatening me, Marc?' The instant the glib words left her lips she was sorry, and her eyes swept upwards in silent contrition—except that it was too late.

There wasn't a thing she could do to stop the unhurried descent of his head, nor evade the vaguely cruel seeking mouth as it fastened unerringly over her own in a kiss that branded her his sole property just as surely as if he had made a public declaration to that effect.

'How could you?' Lee gasped timeless seconds later, and his faint smile was without apology.

'Very easily,' he allowed cynically, adding, 'And with complete enjoyment.'

'Do you realise what you've just done?' she snapped in a furious whisper.

'Was it so terrible?'

His mockery incensed her to a point whereby she found it difficult not to resort to a childish display of temper. 'You're an utter fiend!' she hissed at last. 'If you don't let me go this instant, I'll scream!'

'Then I shall only have to kiss you again,' he drawled. 'Imagine how that will compound our relationship in the eyes of everyone present.'

'I could kill you!' Her eyes flashed with the desire to do just that, and she felt a tremor shake her body as an incredible anger coursed through her veins. Never before had any man goaded her to such extreme lengths.

'Tell me instead what our mutual friend John had to say.'

Lee felt sure he must be aware of her animosity, the utter enmity she felt for him, yet he appeared unperturbed. If anything he found it amusing, and she longed to cause a scene, if only to disconcert him.

'He invited me to dinner with his family tomorrow evening,' she enlightened him in a waspish undertone. 'I accepted. Now will you let me go?'

'Not yet,' Marc refused quietly. 'I'll take you there, seeing that I, too, will be dining with the Conti family.'

'I'd rather walk than go with you!'

His mouth twisted slightly. 'Thirty miles? That would be carrying feminine pique a little too far.'

'You're an arrogant bastard. My God, I hate you!' she whispered bitterly.

Marc's eyes hardened until they resembled granite flints. 'Arrogant, I'll accept. But never insult an Italian's parentage by insinuating that his birth was other than honourable—unless you're very sure of your facts.'

'I won't apologise, because my interpretation of the word is different from yours,' Lee defended stoically.

'I've no intention of shocking the guests by dragging you outside to render the spanking you so richly deserve,' he directed hardily.

'I'm not afraid of you,' Lee declared bravely, oblivious of the latent anger in that powerful body only inches apart from her own.

'Then you should be,' Marc said pitilessly.

For the remainder of the evening Lee felt as if she was the cynosure of all eyes. There wasn't a moment when she didn't feel like screaming as she attempted to talk with Alicia about inconsequential matters that were far removed from anything to do with Marc. Everywhere she turned she could almost feel the physical lance of Daniella's stabbing glance, and sense the abject curiosity of several women's conjecture. It was a damnable situation, from which it was a relief to escape, although it didn't end there, for Alicia's intrigue demanded an answer—several, it transpired.

'What on earth happened between you and Marc?' Lee's loving sister demanded the instant Stefano set the station wagon moving on to the road, and with a heartfelt sigh Lee attempted to give an explanation.

'He was being no more objectionable than usual,' she began, anger still very much to the fore, and Alicia demanded,

'But *why*?'

'I guess I must have said something,' she shrugged. 'And being the man he is, he decided to publicly humiliate me. It's as simple as that.'

'What did you say, for heaven's sake?'

'Several things,' Lee recounted dryly. 'Not all of which I can remember.'

'Hmn,' her older sister commented in monosyllabic disapproval, and Stefano's chuckle and reference to the wedding itself brought about a necessary distraction so that they reached home without once making further reference to Marc Leone.

The farm belonging to the Conti family lay several miles to the west of Dimbulah, and it took more than half an hour to reach it in Marc's powerful car. Lee had predetermined that she would present a polite façade during the entire time she was there, and throughout the drive she had remained silent, incurring an occasional glance of amusement from Marc.

In view of what had taken place the previous evening, Lee was unsure of her reception, and it was immediately apparent on arrival that both Daniella and Marita had decided to treat her as an arch-enemy. John's inherent good manners went well beneath the surface, but she could tell that he was perplexed and unsure how to treat her.

Only Mr and Mrs Conti were oblivious to the undercurrents, and their greeting was warmhearted and generous. Inside the house Lee was led to the lounge and encouraged to accept a glass of wine, and she sipped the pale rosé in the hope it would provide a necessary boost to her shaky composure.

Marc took a seat nearby, his long muscular frame even at ease emanated a raw masculinity that was impossible to ignore. He resembled a lazy jungle cat whose very indolence masked a dangerously lethal instinct and an intrinsic ability to conquer its quarry. Although who or what that was remained a mystery to all except himself.

'John,' Daniella suggested with apparent kindness, 'why don't you show Lee around the farm?'

'Would you like that, Lee?'

Beginning to feel stifled by the atmosphere inside the room, Lee agreed with an alacrity that brought a smile to John's pleasant features, and incurred a faint hardening in the dark eyes of the man seated beside her. But she was beyond caring what Marc thought, and replacing her glass on a nearby table she stood to her feet and followed John outside.

'I fully expected you to ring and say you'd decided not to come tonight,' John began as soon as they were a few yards away from the house.

'For heaven's sake, why?' Lee demanded.

His answering laugh was entirely without humour. 'Marc,' he elaborated simply as he led the way towards a large group of outbuildings situated almost a hundred yards from the house. 'Last night he stamped you as his property as clearly as if he'd made an announcement to that effect.'

Lee felt sickened at his words, and attempted to explain. 'You're wrong,' she began. 'He provoked a wild unreasoning anger that resulted in me being rude,' she added ruefully. 'What you saw was his reaction, and a deliberate attempt to humiliate me for daring to oppose him.'

'And that's all?'

'Yes.' She uttered a brief laugh. 'Please, don't let's mention his name again.' Impulsively she tucked her arm inside his. 'Show me the farm. Have you any chickens or ducklings? I'm completely softhearted when it comes to any of Nature's young.'

They spent a pleasant twenty minutes wandering around the farm, and Lee returned to the house feeling far more relaxed and carefree. On entering the lounge she met Marc's swift appraisal with a deliberately guileless smile, and pushing back an unruly lock of hair behind her ear, she murmured to John,

'Would you mind if I used the bathroom, or somewhere where there's a mirror? The breeze seems to have caught at my hair.'

'You can use my bedroom,' Daniella interposed swiftly. 'I'll show you where it is.'

Lee accepted the offer with a slight smile, then followed the other girl as she led the way to a room at the other end of the house.

'Marc Leone is mine.' The words tumbled out of Daniella's mouth the instant they entered her bedroom, and Lee drew a deep calming breath as she turned to face her.

'Really?' she queried gently, unsure why she was being so evasive.

'Leave him alone,' Daniella said unsteadily. 'You have no right to him—you're only here on holiday.'

Lee slid her fingers through the unruly length of her hair, pushing it into careless order, then she turned from the mirror with a mixture of pity and exasperation.

'For all I know, Marc may want to remain heart-whole and fancy-free,' she said carefully.

'I thought you liked John,' Daniella burst out, and Lee gave a light shrug.

'As you pointed out, I'm on holiday. Besides, a lasting relationship with any man is the farthest thing from my mind—and that includes both your brother and Marc.' She managed a smile and stepped towards the door. 'Shall we return to the lounge?'

There were three other guests for dinner, making a total of ten seated around the long family dining table. The food was excellent, with ravioli to start, followed by chicken and accompanying salad greens. Dessert was a mango chiffon pie served with whipped cream, and Lee expressed her appreciation.

'This really is delicious,' she complimented charmingly. 'Would you mind if I asked for the recipe?'

'Of course not,' Mrs Conti responded, her pleasure at Lee's praise evident. 'I'll write it out for you before you leave.'

'Lee is something of a gourmet cook,' Marc informed them lazily.

'How—unusual,' Marita offered with a trace of spite. 'She doesn't look the domesticated type at all.'

'And you are, of course?' John teased, thus incurring his sister's wrath.

'I can cook just as well as Daniella can,' she declared peevishly, and he laughed.

'I know. I suffered from both your efforts while Mum was visiting her sister in Brisbane for three weeks. Steak and salad every night of the week.'

Daniella pulled a face at him. 'You're perfectly horrid! It wasn't nearly as bad as that.'

'Spread that sort of story around, and I'll never marry them off,' Mr Conti grinned, and his wife lifted her hands in mock-dismay.

'Three children, each of them over twenty-one. As yet, all are unmarried. I'm beginning to despair of ever becoming a grandmother.'

Lee found herself saying in all seriousness, 'Marriage is becoming an outdated institution.'

John began to laugh, his eyes gleaming with amusement as he taunted, 'Are you trying to shock everyone by pretending you'd prefer living in sin to tying the legal knot?'

She gave a rueful grimace in realisation that she'd plunged head first into a controversial subject. 'Not necessarily,' she allowed cautiously. 'I happen to prefer a career.'

'You don't intend to marry at all? A pretty girl like you?' Mrs Conti declared incredulously. 'I don't believe it!'

'What about love?' Marc drawled. 'Doesn't such an emotion fit into your schedule?'

'I deal in reality, not idealism. Love is a euphoristic complexity of emotions no sane person would want to invite.'

'I don't agree,' Marc argued in a silky voice, and she met those dark gleaming eyes with careless disregard.

'If that's so, why haven't you married?'

With indolent ease he reached out a hand and lifted his glass to his lips, took a sip of its contents, then slowly swirled the wine round the base of the glass, his eyes never leaving hers for a second. 'Tell me, Lee,' he taunted softly. 'What qualities would you insist upon in a husband?'

Lee swallowed the sudden lump that rose in her throat. 'Wealth, health and wisdom—in that order,' she quipped lightly. 'Financial security would be my number one priority.'

'That lets me out,' John sighed with an impudent grin, and she laughed.

'Everyone, I imagine. I refuse to settle for anything less than a millionaire.'

'I assume that if one came along, you'd snap him up in a trice?' Marc insisted silkily, and Lee was suddenly aware of the silence surrounding the table.

'Providing he wasn't over fifty, I'd use all my feminine wiles.'

'And what would he get in return, this mythical millionaire?' he pursued relentlessly.

'My loyalty,' she said evenly. 'And fidelity.'

'You'd give up your career, and live wherever he chose to reside?'

'Gladly.' Why was everyone looking so—expectant? The entire conversation was merely humorous conjecture, yet there wasn't a smile to be seen. Almost as if they knew something that she didn't.

'And marry at short notice?'

'Why would there be any reason to wait?'

'Thank you, Lee,' Marc acknowledged mockingly.

His dark gleaming gaze swept round the table. 'Congratulations are in order, don't you agree?'

Lee frowned, then vaguely disquieted, she demanded, 'What do you mean?'

Marc's smile was frankly cynical, his eyes deadly. 'You've just agreed to become my wife.'

Lee heard the words, but for a few seconds they failed to register, then, sure the whole thing was a hoax, she allowed her mouth to relax into a warm smile. Whatever game he was playing, she was determined to call his bluff. 'How can I be sure you qualify?' she challenged.

His eyes never left her face. 'Everyone in this room will attest that what I've said is true. For additional verification, you have only to ask your sister and brother-in-law.'

Somehow she managed to control an awful sense of foreboding that rose like gall in her throat. 'I think this joke has gone far enough,' she voiced unsteadily, and glimpsed his twisted smile.

'I wasn't joking, Lee.'

Slowly she let her gaze wander round the table, seeing with frightening clarity the answer reflected in everyone's face. 'I need a drink,' she said shakily, trying to buy time in which to think. For the life of her she couldn't recall exactly what she had said. As far as she was concerned the whole conversation had begun as a farcical episode that had roots in a childish vow she had evolved somewhere around the age of twelve. Just how foolish—and dangerous—she was yet to discover!

'Refill your glasses,' Mr Conti bade heartily, being among the first to recover. 'We must drink a toast to Marc and Lee's future happiness.'

Everyone looked stunned, but none more so than Lee, who was beginning to believe she had dreamed the whole thing.

Somehow Marc was standing beside her, his arm curving round her waist in support, and a glass of wine was placed in her hand.

'Drink some,' he bade quietly. 'You're as pale as a ghost.'

'Shock,' Lee murmured. 'Am I supposed to smile?'

'It would help. I'm not exactly Bluebeard.'

'This is insane,' she whispered tentatively. 'How can you——'

'Save the arguments for later.'

The wine helped to provide a necessary haze in which Lee managed to pass the ensuing hour and a half before Marc declared it was time for them to leave. Worst of all had been the look of reproach on John's kindly face, and secondly, the thinly-disguised rage that was directed towards her from both Daniella and Marita.

It was with considerable relief that Lee bade Mr and Mrs Conti goodnight and followed Marc out to the car. The silence stretched from five minutes into ten as the large vehicle sped quickly through the dark countryside.

'Nothing to say, Lee?' Marc drawled, and she slowly turned to face him.

'I'm speechless,' she answered wryly.

'Incredible,' he slanted sardonically. 'I expected a verbal onslaught at the very least.'

'When do you intend telling them the truth?'

'What truth?' he queried uncompromisingly.

She rounded on him in utter exasperation. 'That we're not really engaged, of course!'

'Wrong,' Marc disputed in a dangerously quiet voice. 'There were several witnesses to my proposition—and your acceptance.'

'You can't mean to say you were serious?' Lee demanded incredulously.

'Perfectly. Weren't you?'

'*No*. The whole thing was just a joke!'

'By midday tomorrow the grapevine will have successfully taken care of the problem,' he shrugged wryly. 'To add fuel to the proverbial fire, my mother is due to arrive in Cairns on the late afternoon flight from Sydney. We'll drive down to Cairns after lunch, shop for an engagement ring, then meet the plane. She'll be delighted,' he slanted musingly, 'having despaired of ever seeing me married. I'm organising a barbecue on Tuesday evening to welcome home a very good friend of mine who's been overseas for several years. It will be an excellent opportunity to announce our pending marriage.'

'Hey, just a minute!' Lee expostulated. 'I'm not coming to Cairns with you, nor am I going to be presented to your mother as your—fiancée!' Her eyes glittered with a bitter consuming anger. 'And if you dare to make any announcement, I'll deny it. I will!' she threatened wildly, and clenched her hands together tightly in her lap to prevent from lashing out at him.

Minutes later the car slowed and turned off the main road, and Lee swung round to face him.

'Where are we? Why are you stopping?' she demanded trenchantly, and her heart almost faltered and stopped at the expression on his face. Grim and forbidding, he positively frightened her as he brought the car to a halt and switched off the ignition.

'Come inside, Lee. I'll make some coffee, and we'll talk.'

'I'm not getting out of this car!'

Marc gave an exasperated sigh that behoved great forbearance. 'This is my farm,' he declared brusquely, and leaned an arm on the steering wheel as he turned towards her. 'I'd prefer to conduct this discussion inside the house.' His lips twisted into a cynical smile. 'Rest assured I have no ulterior motive in mind. You're quite safe, Lee,' he drawled.

Am I? she thought wryly. My emotions are in a bad enough state as it is, but whenever we're alone they shred into a thousand pieces.

To refuse to go inside would seem churlish—and childish. 'Very well,' she agreed, reaching for the door clasp. 'But not for long.'

Marc didn't answer, and with a feeling of trepidation she slid out of the car and followed him towards the long sprawling dwelling situated several yards distant.

The moonlight cast long dark shadows, and Lee gave an involuntary start as a canine growl sounded far too close for comfort.

'Quiet, Bruno!' Marc ordered, and the animal immediately subsided with a whimper. 'Alsatian,' he revealed as he led the way indoors. 'I have two.'

'Security?' she tendered briefly. 'Out here?'

He switched on lights, providing a welcome illuminating glow, and his expression assumed sardonic amusement as he paused for her to reach his side. 'There's a lot of expensive equipment on a farm this size. Machinery alone runs into several thousands of dollars.' He gestured towards a spacious, comfortably furnished room. 'Go and sit down. I'll set up the percolator.'

Lee glanced around with interest, noting that for a bachelor establishment it was extremely well kept. Loath to sit alone, she followed him through what was obviously the dining-room and into the kitchen. A gleam of appreciation lit her eyes as she took in the modern styling. It was a housewife's dream, with a wall oven, ceramic-topped counters, capacious refrigerator and deep-freeze, and a dishwasher. There were an abundance of cupboards, a central work-table, and sufficient electrical gadgets to please the most fastidious of women.

'Like it?'

At the sound of his drawling query, Lee swept her gaze towards him. 'Who wouldn't?' she answered simply, and he inclined his head.

'Do you want a conducted tour over the rest of the house?'

'No—thank you.' She summoned forth a slight smile. 'I imagine it has the usual number of rooms.'

Marc removed the lid of the percolator, spooned in a quantity of ground coffee beans, added water, then flicked the switch before turning back to face her.

'Plus a few added advantages,' he told her. 'A billiard room, sauna and spa pool—for my mother's benefit. She suffers from rheumatism.'

Lee swallowed convulsively. She felt ill at ease, and very much aware of the powerful magnetism he projected. When he chose, Marc could exert a practised charm to which she was particularly vulnerable. It was almost as if he had the power to reach out and touch her without even moving a muscle. As a lover he would be dynamic, combining tenderness with a hint of cruelty, a savage passion that could wreak havoc with an inexperienced heart. To love such a man would be folly—a one-way path to self-destruction.

'Have I suddenly grown a beard?' Marc taunted, running a hand along his jaw, and his eyes gleamed with quizzical laughter as a faint tinge of pink coloured her cheeks.

Lee held his gaze, determined not to let him see how unsettled she was, and her voice was even as she queried, 'What game are you playing, Marc?'

'What makes you think I'm playing a game?' he countered, and she drew a deep uneven breath.

'You deliberately and very cleverly led me into an argument earlier this evening. The entire conversation revolved round a hypothetical circumstance, and you know it.'

He thrust hands into his trouser pockets and let his eyes roam at will over her slender frame, lingering with indolent insolence on the slight rise and fall of her breasts beneath the thin silk blouse before travelling slowly up to her mouth, then coming to rest on the twin points of gold fury glaring at him with indignation.

'You're the first woman I've offered to marry,' Marc told her with amused cynicism, and Lee thrust her hands behind her back as she clenched them together in nervous tension.

'Why? Dear God, am I supposed to be honoured?'

His eyes held hers relentlessly, their gleaming depths darkly brilliant, and the edges of his mouth twisted into a slight musing smile. 'It's quite simple,' he drawled. 'I want you.'

Lee momentarily closed her eyes and simultaneously took a backward step. 'Why—marriage?' she demanded unsteadily. 'I can't imagine you experiencing any difficulty getting a woman into bed.' She gave a hollow laugh, and her eyes assumed a wild expression. 'Daniella and Marita would leap at the chance!'

He inclined his head in silent mocking agreement. 'But not you, Lee—eh?'

'How can you know that?'

His humourless laugh was faintly derisive. 'I haven't reached the age of thirty-five without gaining a vast experience of women.'

'And you're always right, of course!'

'Invariably,' he mocked relentlessly. 'We wouldn't be having this conversation if I was wrong.'

A sudden bubble of uncontrollable laughter escaped her lips. 'Perhaps you should try harder. You might succeed in wearing down my resistance.'

'Is that an admission?'

The laughter choked to a halt. 'No—damn you!' Her voice emerged as a stricken whisper. The need to get away from him was paramount, and without thinking she turned and ran.

Hard hands caught hold of her shoulders before she had taken more than a few steps, and she struggled impotently, experiencing a mixture of fear and unaccountable rage. There wasn't a thing she could do to effect an escape, and after a few minutes she gave up even trying, resigning herself to stand quiescent within his encircling arms.

Subtly his powerful grip eased, and he slowly turned her round to face him, lifting her chin so that she had to look at him.

'Let me go, Marc,' she pleaded shakily, her eyes widening into pools of deep topaz as she met his inscrutable gaze.

'What are you afraid of, Lee?' he demanded quietly. 'Me—or yourself?'

She wanted to scream at him that it was both—but most of all it was her own wayward emotions she wanted to rage against. Some of the conflict must have been evident in her expressive features, for suddenly she was free, and she flinched as he lifted an idle hand and pushed back a lock of her hair that had fallen forward into tumbled disarray.

'Coffee,' he directed wryly. 'It'll create a necessary diversion.'

'I'd rather go home, if you don't mind.'

His mouth twisted into the semblance of a smile. 'Soon, I give you my word. But first we must clear up a few points.'

'You can explain that it was all a mistake,' Lee ventured. 'Blame it on me.'

'This is something I take full responsibility for,' Marc declared dryly. 'A month from now you will have achieved your objective.'

'But I don't want to get married—much less to you!' she cried. 'It would be like living with—with dynamite,' she added wildly.

His laughter began deep in his chest, then rumbled to the surface in genuine amusement. 'At first, perhaps,' he allowed devilishly. 'But afterwards it will be very good—I promise,' he added softly.

'There's more to marriage than sexual satisfaction,' Lee vented swiftly. 'And what about children?' she asked in desperation. 'I'm not ready to make that sort of commitment.'

'You already have, in a way I consider irrevocable.'

'But you can't hold me to it!' she exclaimed. 'I'll explain——'

'Too late,' he declared implacably. 'By tomorrow most people will have heard of our engagement. To deny it so soon will only raise doubts as to your——'

'Sanity?' Lee demanded, anger uppermost. 'You hold all the cards, don't you?' she accused bitterly.

'The important ones,' he acknowledged.

'So, to prevent myself from appearing an utter fool, I become engaged to you,' she said heavily. 'For how long, Marc?'

'As long as it takes,' he answered cynically, and she deliberated silently, trying to find some rational remedy.

The thought occurred that she had only two weeks left of her holiday. After she had returned to Sydney it would be relatively easy for Marc to explain that the bogus engagement was over. Suddenly the solution seemed so simple she almost laughed out loud.

'I don't have much choice, do I?' she capitulated reluctantly.

Marc merely smiled, and reaching into a nearby cupboard he withdrew cups and saucers and placed them beside the percolator. 'Sugar? Milk or cream?' he asked blandly, and she answered abstractedly, following him into the lounge when he had poured their coffee.

'If I'm to meet your mother,' Lee began after taking a few sips from her cup, 'shouldn't I know more about you?'

His gaze was openly sardonic. 'Statistics?'

'She'll think it strange that I know practically nothing of your family background,' she declared wryly, shooting him a dark glance. 'Imagine being presented with a girl purported to be your son's fiancée who is ignorant of everything except his name, age and financial status!'

Marc drained the contents of his cup and set it

down on a nearby table, then he leaned back against the cushioned sofa exuding a relaxed ease Lee would have dearly liked to emulate.

'My father died ten years ago,' he told her lazily, his dark eyes inscrutable as he regarded her. 'I had just begun to carve a niche for myself as a business consultant in Sydney, which of necessity had to be shelved for a few years while I came home and took over the reins on the farm. When my sister married and moved down south, Mother missed her terribly, so at my suggestion she now divides her time equally between us. The farm is set up as a family trust, and run very profitably with the assistance of a manager who resides on the property. He's employed on a salary basis with a share of the profits, which ensures that he works very hard to achieve success,' he revealed dryly. 'He's responsible for employing workers and cultivating the crop, which enables me to be absent for as long and as often as I choose. Consequently I manage to direct my own consultancy firm in Sydney for several months of each year,' he concluded, and Lee met his level gaze unflinchingly.

'Am I to surmise that you're not wholly enamoured of farm life?' she queried lightly, and his answering laughter was husky and faintly dry.

'I was born on this farm. For almost as long as I can remember, tobacco has played a large part in my life, although not necessarily by choice. Hence a privileged education in boarding schools and university. If it wasn't for my mother's sentimental attachment I would have sold the farm years ago.' He gave a careless shrug. 'As it is, I manage to combine both interests with some success.'

'You're very fond of your mother, aren't you?'

'She's a very special lady,' Marc declared significantly. 'I would like your word that you won't do or say anything to cause her distress.'

Lee looked at him carefully. 'Do you expect me to portray a loving fiancée?'

His smile was faintly quizzical. 'Will you find that so difficult?'

She finished the last of her coffee and replaced the cup on to its saucer, then stood to her feet. 'I'd like to go home. It's quite late, and I'm tired.' Without waiting she walked out to the kitchen and placed the cup and saucer in the sink.

'In so much of a hurry to get away from me?'

Lee turned round to face him, and her heart skipped a beat at his close proximity. 'Please, Marc!' Her nerve-ends began to tingle as he leaned forward and caught hold of her chin.

'You'll behave yourself for my mother's benefit?'

'I'm not totally insensitive.'

'I didn't say you were,' he said wryly, and she shifted her gaze to a point beyond his shoulder.

'Can we go now?' If she didn't get away from him soon she'd scream! Every nerve and fibre cried out for his touch, and she had to physically restrain herself from swaying towards him.

Without a word Marc turned and led the way out to the car, and Lee slid into the passenger seat with profound relief. The distance of half a mile was covered in a matter of minutes, and as soon as the tires crunched to a halt she reached for the door clasp.

'No goodnight kiss?' Marc mocked in a husky drawl, and she reiterated fiercely,

'There's no one around to see.'

'I'll take one just the same.'

VISIT 4 MAGIC PLACES
FREE

PORTUGAL

TEXAS

SWEET REVENGE by Anne Mather
When Antonia innocently became part of an attempted swindle, Raoul planned to carry out his "sweet revenge." She fled from his exquisite castle in Portugal, but Raoul, used to having his way with women, found her.

NO QUARTER ASKED by Janet Dailey
All Stacy had been looking for was a place to sort things out for herself. But the beautiful invalid had not reckoned on the ruggedly handsome Cord Harris, powerful Texan cattle baron.

CYPRUS

FRANCE

GATES OF STEEL by Anne Hampson
Disenchanted with love, Helen fled to exotic Cyprus, only to encounter the handsome, arrogant Leon Petrou. His proposal of marriage surprised Helen, but she accepted. It would be solely a marriage of convenience, she thought. But Helen was wrong.

DEVIL IN A SILVER ROOM by Violet Winspear
Paul Cassailis, master of the remote French chateau of Satancourt, desired the quiet, reserved Margo. But love had brought Margo pain once before. Now Paul stood accused of murder. And Margo discovered to her horror that she loved him.

Love surrounds you in the pages of Harlequin romances

Harlequin Presents romance novels are the ultimate in romantic fiction... the kind of stories that you can't put down... that take you to romantic places in search of adventure and intrigue. They are stories full of the emotions of love... full of the hidden turmoil beneath even the most innocent-seeming relationships. Desperate clinging love, emotional conflict, bold lovers, destructive jealousies and romantic imprisonment—you'll find it all in the passionate pages of **Harlequin Presents** romance novels.

Let your imagination roam to the far ends of the earth. Meet true-to-life people. Become intimate with those who live larger than life.

Harlequin Presents romance novels are the kind of books you just can't put down... the kind of experiences that remain in your dreams long after you've read about them.

TAKE THESE **4** BEST-SELLING
HARLEQUIN ROMANCES

FREE SEE EXCITING
DETAILS INSIDE

'You're insufferable!' she choked, hating him at that moment.

'You protest too much,' he chided pitilessly as he leaned forward and brushed his lips across her cheekbone. His mouth captured hers in a hard compelling kiss that lent no pretence to gentleness, then she was free. 'Tomorrow,' he reminded her deliberately. 'One o'clock.'

Lee refrained from slamming the car door behind her, and forced herself to walk up the few steps to the front door instead of running as she would have liked to do.

In her bedroom she sank down on to the bed in a gesture of defeat. She felt completely enervated, and instinctively certain that she had unwittingly played right into Marc's hands. With a weariness that had little to do with lack of sleep she slipped off her shoes and changed out of her clothes, then slid between the sheets in the hope that the dark curtain of sleep would obliterate the evening's events, for she had no desire to dwell on the consequences.

CHAPTER SIX

As Marc had predicted, news in a small community spread with amazing speed, and when he called to collect Lee shortly after lunch for the drive down to Cairns her greeting was superficially warm.

'That smile of yours is quite something,' he observed musingly as he set the sleek Fairlane moving swiftly out on to the main road. 'You should do it more often.'

Lee shot him a wry glance. 'Do you realise what you've done?'

'You refer to our engagement?'

'What else?' Her eyes sparkled with pent-up rage. 'My sister has waxed lyrical over the news from the time the phone first rang just after breakfast.' Her voice rose a fraction. 'Have you any conception what I've had to put up with?' Her eyes rose heavenward in pious supplication. 'My God! If I had stayed in that house another minute I would have exploded!'

'As bad as that?' Marc queried sardonically, and she could cheerfully have hit him for displaying such cynical amusement.

'You've stirred up a hornets' nest,' Lee snapped with asperity, 'and put me right in the midst of it. Alicia must have taken twenty calls this morning—all from women demanding to know if her sister had worked some mystical spell over a man they considered to be their particular property! It must be some harem you keep,' she finished with ill-disguised bitterness.

'I plead guilty to a collection of female friends,' he drawled mockingly. 'But referring to them as part of a harem is totally erroneous.'

'You surprise me,' she commented with marked sarcasm. 'I'm labelled as some sort of libellous witch, while you emerge scot-free. If this morning was anything to go by, I feel inclined to wear a placard around my neck with the words "not guilty" emblazoned in huge lettering.'

'My mother will love you.'

'Thanks,' she said dryly. 'That thought cheers me no end.'

'So it should.'

Lee glanced across the space between them, her expression speculative. 'You seem inordinately attached to her.'

'Most Italians are very family-conscious,' he explained tolerantly. 'Children are the focal point of their parents' existence. It's a philosophy gained from age-old tradition.' His wide mouth curved into a softened smile. 'I think you'll see what I mean when you meet her.'

'You were horribly spoilt,' Lee proclaimed, and incurred his laughter.

'Quite the opposite,' Marc said wryly. 'I had to work doubly hard to achieve any favours, owing to my father's wealth. Everything received was earned the hard way, and I was taught never to take anything for granted.'

'A spartan upbringing.' It explained the vague cruelty, the worldly cynicism in his manner.

'Necessary,' he shrugged indolently. 'It achieved its objective.'

When they reached Cairns Marc parked the car in the main street, then he leaned across to unlock her door. The slight contact sent goose-bumps shivering down her spine, and she slid quickly from the car to pause on the pavement as she waited for him to join her.

Tall and lithely built, with his rugged looks he did strange things to her equilibrium. For one brief minute she almost wished there was some sentiment motivating the purchase of a ring. Then she quickly stifled such thoughts, mentally questioning her sanity. Marc Leone was the last man she would think of marrying!

'Any particular preference as to stones or design?'

Lee looked at him blankly for a few seconds, then as his words penetrated, she gave a slight shrug. 'What does it matter? Something inexpensive.'

Marc's grip on her elbow tightened fractionally as he led her into an elegantly appointed showroom, and his presence elicited the immediate solicitous attention of the manager.

'Mr Leone! How can we help you?'

Lee darted Marc a faint smile, her eyes frankly mocking as she deduced the reason for his frequent patronage. 'Gifts of jewellery for services rendered—darling?' she mumured the instant the manager was out of hearing.

'Careful, my sweet,' Marc warned dangerously. 'I'm not beyond quieting that vicious little tongue of yours.'

'And shock that poor man?' she effused prettily. 'Marc, how could you!'

His dark glance had a riveting effect. 'Very easily,' he answered, and her eyes became faintly mutinous. 'Stop it, Lee,' he cautioned. 'I don't make idle threats.'

'I stand in fear and trembling,' she responded wryly, then gave a faint gasp as he bent down and took her mouth in a kiss that was mercilessly hard. 'You bastard!' she whispered through bruised lips, then her eyes widened in disbelief as he deliberately brought his mouth down again in pitiless resolve.

'I warned you about the careless use of that particular word,' he declared silkily, and it was all she could do not to lash out at him.

'I'm sorry for the delay. This selection had to be retrieved from our vault. It's not often we have a call for such high quality gems.'

Lee stared blankly ahead, dimly aware of Marc and the manager as they conferred over the contents on the black velvet tray that had been placed on top of the counter. Twin spots of colour burned brightly on her cheeks, and it took all her resolve not to turn and walk away. A hollow laugh rose silently in her throat. Where could she go that he wouldn't follow? Marc Leone observed no conventional rules whatsoever.

'Yes, the solitaire,' Marc instructed. 'As you say, it's flawless and expertly cut. I like its fiery yellow sparkle. It reminds me of my fiancée's eyes. Try it on, darling.'

Lee turned towards him, her tortured gaze centring on the ring he held out, then it swung rapidly upwards to meet those dark mocking depths. Without a word she obediently held out her hand for him to slip it on, although she inwardly cringed from the contact of cold metal against her finely-boned finger. It felt like a manacle, and for a wild uncontrollable moment she experienced the feeling that it was there to stay.

'The young lady has very delicate hands. The ring will need to be correctly sized,' the manager ventured, and Marc gave a brief affirmative nod.

'I trust you can attend to it this afternoon? Shall we say—four o'clock?'

'It's far too expensive,' Lee burst out the instant they were out of the shop.

'A ring is essential,' Marc declared bluntly as he led her towards the car. 'Aren't you forgetting it will be examined, assessed and admired countless times by family—yours, and mine—not to mention an abundance of friends?' He unlocked the door and held it open as she slid inside, then he strode round and slipped in behind the wheel.

'Of course,' Lee murmured bitterly, and her eyes glittered with ill-concealed animosity, 'I should have remembered your elevated status in the community. A paltry bauble would hardly be fitting for the fiancée of Marc Leone, would it?' Her eyes swept up to meet his. 'I shall have to endeavour to do it justice—although I can't promise I won't feel tempted to wrench it off! I dislike being branded as any man's exclusive property. Especially yours,' she finished resentfully.

For a few timeless seconds the air was perfectly still, then in seemingly slow motion his head lowered, his hands moving to hold her prisoner as he kissed her. There was a leashed savagery in the way his mouth forced hers apart, and she was powerless to stop the plundering force that threatened to devour her very soul. If he had wanted to wound her deeply he could not have chosen a better method than that cruel public demonstration.

When at last he pulled back, her eyes were large shimmering pools of drowning topaz in a face that had become pale and strained. Worst of all was her mouth, bruised, faintly swollen, and trembling with a kind of numbed pain that seemed to be slowly spreading over her entire body.

'*Dio!*' Marc murmured huskily as he raked her whitened features, then with a gesture of restrained violence he leant forward and ignited the powerful engine, reversing expertly before swinging the large car into the stream of traffic.

Lee sat in a state of suspended limbo, too enervated to take note of where they were heading. She told herself she didn't really care. Oh God, her head ached. Her whole body, in fact. Shakily she lifted a hand to her temple, resting her elbow against the car door for support as she turned unseeing eyes out over the swiftly passing hinterland. Wearily she closed her eyes, hoping to blot out the hard indomitable features that seemed to have etched themselves permanently in her brain. Somehow she stirred alive a latent cruelty that was almost primitive. Never had she felt so vulnerable, so ready to weep, in her entire life.

Lee wasn't even aware that the car slowed and came to a halt until she felt a hand brush back a length of hair behind her ear, and she turned with sudden fear, her eyes focusing with difficulty on the harsh planes of Marc's compelling features.

She felt the touch of his fingers as they trailed gently over the delicate bones of her face, and gave an involuntary shiver as they slowly traced the outline of her bruised mouth.

'Don't!' The tortured sound left her lips as a barely audible whisper that went on to beg, 'Please—leave me alone.'

'Do you think I haven't tried?' Marc queried wryly as he moved to cup her face with his hands. 'I'm continually torn between the desire to hurt and kiss you.'

'You do both—with unparalleled excellence,' she accorded shakily, and her whole body began to tremble as he moved close.

'You realise there can be only one remedy?' His eyes had become so dark she felt she might drown in them, and she made one futile attempt to escape. Only it was too late—way too late.

His mouth touched hers briefly with such incredible gentleness it was all she could do not to cry. Then, feather-light, it travelled up to press closed each eyelid in turn before seeking first the sensitive curve of her ear, stirring alive a warm sensual flame as he nuzzled the lobe and the delicate hollows beneath. Slowly, achingly, his lips continued their devastating trail down the sensitive cord of her neck, wandered at will over the fine bones at the base of her throat before travelling up the other side to render similar treatment, until with a tormented groan Lee twisted her head so that her mouth could meet those seeking lips.

Never in her life had she been kissed quite like this, for it was like being made love to—an ultimate experience in erotic seductiveness, so incredibly sweet that she never wanted it to end. It was Marc who was in total control, moulding her mouth with his own, shaping it, probing with infinite sensitivity, obliterating past onslaughts as he sought to appease and arouse her bruised emotions.

When at last he lifted his head, it was she who moved to recapture his mouth, and her eyes wore a faintly bewildered air as he gently disentangled her arms from about his neck.

'You're beautiful,' Marc said quietly, and his eyes roved in a slow intimate appraisal that brought a blush to her cheeks.

Lee shook her head, and attempted to fight off the feeling of bemusement that seemed to have settled upon her. 'I had too many years at school being called alternatively "Red" and "Carrots" to believe that,' she volunteered solemnly, and gave a wry smile at his faint chuckle. 'Really,' she assured him.

'Your skin is the colour of pure honey and quite without freckles.'

She wrinkled her nose and a mischievous sparkle lit her eyes. 'Oh, I have a few,' she told him. 'In places hidden from general view.'

'Hm,' Marc pondered teasingly. 'I shall take delight in discovering them for myself when we have more privacy. Be warned I intend kissing each and every one of them.' His eyes gleamed with wicked devilry, and she had to look away, flustered and embarrassed at the mere thought of him placing his mouth there.

'What time is it? Don't you think we should be going?' The words came out in a slight rush as she struggled to sit upright in her seat.

'Unused to conducting intimate conversation with a man, Lee?' he slanted with a trace of mockery.

'Good heavens, no,' she assured him far too quickly. 'I'm quite wordly-wise and unshockable.'

His eyes darkened measurably as he took her chin between thumb and forefinger, tilting it so she had to look at him. 'If I thought that, I'd make you beg for mercy.'

Lee swallowed convulsively. 'Stop it, Marc,' she pleaded shakily. 'Right at this moment I don't possess the strength to fight you.'

'My, my, is that an admission?'

For a long time Lee could only look at him, then she offered carefully, 'You have the advantage of superior physical strength, a sophisticated life style I couldn't hope to emulate despite having lived in a city most of my life. Besides, you seem to delight in deliberately taunting me,' she added. 'Almost as if you want to drive me to the very limit of my endurance. How do you expect me to react? With a limpid smile as I turn the other cheek?'

'That would be totally out of character,' Marc declared, and bending forward he kissed her briefly before straightening back in his seat. 'Come on, let's walk for a while, then we'll head back to town.'

The immediate surroundings had escaped her, but now Lee glanced out of the window with interest and saw that they were parked in a small layby near the caravan park at Ellis Beach. There was a path leading down on to the sand, and she slipped from the car and began walking through the encroaching undergrowth.

It was a lovely day, the sun beginning to lower in an azure sky, but to her unacclimatised skin it felt warm despite the slight breeze that feathered gently against her, tugging her hair into attractive disarray as she reached the foreshore. Without thought she bent down and removed her slim-heeled sandals, then holding them in one hand she wandered down towards the water.

Blue and inviting, the tide was on the turn, its incoming vigour dispersing, and Lee gave in to an uncommon urge to feel the wet sand beneath her toes.

'Are you trying to get rid of me?'

Feeling free and energised, she glanced round and laughed, her eyes frankly teasing as she took in his immaculate trousers and shoe-shod feet.

'Be daring,' she suggested quizzically. 'Roll up your trousers and come with me.'

'You're an impudent child,' he grinned. 'But I'll try to be indulgent.'

'How uncharacteristic of you,' she smiled, holding out her hand. 'If you hurry, I'll wait for you.'

His quiet chuckle brought a sudden knot in her stomach. If only she could capture this moment and preserve it! He was an enigma—so vital he appeared almost invincible, with a strength and virility that was frightening. Yet there were times when he exhibited unexpected gentleness, and she wondered rather sadly if she really knew him at all.

'Tell me about your childhood.'

Lee felt her hand become lost inside his large one, and she turned to gaze out towards the horizon. 'There's not much to tell,' she said evenly. 'My father died shortly after I was born, leaving my mother to cope as best she could with two young children. Despite being relatively poor, Alicia and I had a happy childhood. Mother refused to go out to work and leave us in anyone's care, so she took in sewing at home to earn sufficient money to pay the rent and feed and clothe us.'

'Were there no relatives who could have helped?'

Lee shook her head. 'Dad's parents lived out west,' she explained matter-of-factly. 'I believe they were well off, and didn't approve of their son marrying a city girl whom they considered not nearly good enough for him. After his funeral, my mother never heard from them again. Sad, really,' she declared pensively. 'I was only fourteen when she died, but I remember her being full of fun and life. Alicia and I may not have had much in the way of material possessions, but we had all the loving care it was possible to have.'

'And afterwards?' Marc prompted.

'Alicia was already working,' she revealed slowly. 'And I left school just as soon as I could. An apprentice hairdresser's wage is fairly meagre, but we managed between us. Then Alicia met Stefano when he was in Sydney on holiday, and they married soon after.'

'Which left you to cope alone at what—sixteen?'

'I wasn't exactly helpless,' Lee protested. 'Alicia and Stefano wanted me to move north and live with them for a while, but I couldn't have done that.

Besides, I had a natural talent with hair, and a vision of climbing out of mediocrity. Living in a small country town was hardly conducive to furthering a successful career.'

'And is it?'

She glanced upwards and met his dark inscrutable gaze. 'I like to think so. I've worked hard and saved every cent I can. In another year I should have sufficient money to buy my own salon. Oh, not in the city itself,' she added wryly. 'But a few years on the outskirts and I should be able to choose one of the wealthier inner suburbs. Then I shall really achieve my objective.'

'Double Bay, perhaps? I have an apartment there,' Marc revealed, and Lee gave a slight grimace.

'Very nice,' she said ruefully. 'I suppose it's a penthouse suite commanding a fabulous view.' Her eyes lit with faint irony. 'Ideal for entertaining your numerous women friends.'

'Of course,' he answered humorously. 'Although I prefer one at a time—orgies tend to be exhausting.'

The thought of him with another woman made her feel physically ill, and in a strained little voice she said, 'Let's go back.' Unconsciously she tugged at her hand, wanting to be free of him. The peace they had shared was broken, and a lot of her former antipathy returned. 'We have to make ourselves presentable to meet your mother. I don't imagine she would appreciate bare feet and windblown hair,' she concluded dryly.

'Was it a reference to orgies, I wonder?' Marc questioned mildly. 'Surely you recognise a joke?' His amusement was evident, and she felt her stomach muscles tighten painfully.

'Of course. Even the great Marcello Leone isn't superhuman,' she mocked, and glimpsed his broad frame shake shake with silent laughter.

'We're back to square one, I take it?'

'Were we ever out of it?' she countered, and he paused briefly to pull her close against him.

'Oh yes, my sweet.' His breath fanned tendrils of hair that lay across her forehead, then his mouth was on hers, possessive and frighteningly knowledgeable as it moved back and forth in a manner that was disruptively sensual.

Lee was silent during the short drive back to Cairns, and she endeavoured to hide her reluctance as Marc slid the magnificent solitaire diamond on to her finger.

'We've time for a quick drink before heading out to the airport,' he indicated as he led her along the pavement, and Lee inclined her head in silent apathy.

'Champagne,' he decided, giving the order the instant they were seated in a nearby hotel lounge.

When her glass was filled, Lee sipped the contents and let her gaze wander idly as she attempted to gather together some courage. If Marc's mother was anything like him, she felt she needed all the help she could get.

'So quiet,' Marc mocked with a trace of cynicism. 'What's going on inside that head of yours?'

Lee glanced down at the exquisite ring splaying a myriad brilliant colours from its many facets. 'I should thank you,' she proffered solemnly. 'No one could doubt its excellence. It's perfectly splendid.'

'I'm glad you approve,' he inclined dryly.

'No, really,' she said with quiet sincerity. 'It's precisely what one would expect from a man of your wealth and position. I shall guard it carefully.' And return it just as soon as this fiasco has reached its conclusion, she added silently.

'Drink up, Lee,' Marc instructed brusquely. 'I realise you're a bundle of nerves at the prospect of meeting my mother, but right at this moment I'm having
the greatest difficulty in restraining myself from
giving you a good slap.'

Lee's tension increased measurably as she stood by
Marc's side watching the stream of passengers vacate
the large Boeing, and any preconceived ideas she had
about Mrs Leone were dashed to the ground as a slim,
middle-aged woman separated herself from the crowd.

'Marc! How good it is to see you again!' Light grey
eyes creased with ill-disguised affection as she presented first one cheek and then the other for his warm
embrace. 'Lee, my dear—how are you?' The smile she
gave was genuine, and without ceremony she leaned
forward and afforded her son's fiancée an unaffected
greeting. 'I can see why Marc felt compelled to sweep
you off your feet.' She looked from one to the other of
them and gave a gentle laugh before turning back to
Lee. 'Welcome to the family, Lee.'

Lee felt as if her powers of speech had temporarily
deserted her, and the smile she gave Mrs Leone was
slightly hesitant.

'You have no idea how nervous she's been,' Marc
remarked, and his mouth twitched with humour as he
slipped an arm across Lee's shoulders, then according
his mother the same gesture, he turned and moved
towards the luggage bay.

'I'm not surprised,' Mrs Leone laughed softly, sparing him a somewhat wry smile. 'You're every bit as
forceful as your dear father was. I can imagine Lee
wondering what sort of woman mothered you!'

Marc's husky laughter brought forth an infectious

grin from that good lady, and Lee could only wonder that this was the same man who had shown her such unprincipled passion. Startling, too, was the knowledge that he had given his mother advance warning of the engagement.

The luggage stowed in the trunk, Marc set the car in motion and moved out from the airport terminal on to the main highway heading west towards the Kuranda Ranges. Conversation became a sparkling exchange between mother and son, into which Lee was drawn with a naturalness that wasn't feigned, so that she began to feel a warm affinity towards the woman who made no secret of her delight over her son's pending marriage. Consequently the hour's drive to Mareeba seemed to take scarcely any time at all, although it was with a sense of relief that Lee viewed their imminent arrival.

'You'll stay for dinner, Lee?' Mrs Leone glimpsed her slight hesitation, and insisted charmingly, 'Oh, please do. We have so much to talk about.'

That's debatable, Lee brooded, unsure that a tête-à-tête with Marc's mother was a wise move, yet it would seem churlish to refuse. 'That would be lovely,' she accepted politely.

The large car slowed and turned into the driveway, to come to a halt beside the paved path leading up to the house.

'I love coming home,' Mrs Leone enthused, and cast her gaze over the neatly-cut lawn surrounding the large sprawling dwelling. Turning slightly, she captured Lee's attention. 'My late husband acquired this land through a Goverment-sponsored ballot more than thirty years ago. Do you see that house just beyond the barns? That was our first home, built originally as three rooms and added to five years later, and yet again. This place,' she indicated the modern brick structure immediately in front of them, 'comprises everything I ever dreamed of, and is the culmination of many hours spent poring over countless plans, designs and samples. The irony of it is that the house was only completed a year before my husband's death, so he had little opportunity to witness my enjoyment of it.'

Lee made an appropriate murmuring comment as she walked with the other woman towards the front door, remarking on the splendidly kept garden and flower borders that lined the path.

'Yes, they are lovely, aren't they?' Mrs Leone agreed. 'With practically no rainfall throughout most of the year it's impossible to grow anything without constant water-sprinkling, but the tropics lend themselves to an abundance of colourful blooms that make the effort rewarding.'

On reaching the tiled verandah Mrs Leone paused to extract a key, then pulling back the insect screen she unlocked the door and stood aside for Lee to precede her.

Marc followed immediately at their rear with a suitcase in each hand. 'I'll take these through to your room, then we'll have a drink.'

Lee avoided his eyes, and directed a smile somewhere in the vicinity of his chin.

'Now, my dear, let me look at you,' said Mrs Leone the instant her son was out of sight. Her smile was warm, her expression sincere as she reached out and caught hold of Lee's hands. 'You don't know how glad I am that Marc has finally decided to get married.' She gave a tinkling laugh that was infectious. 'I'd almost given up, believe me!'

This was going from bad to worse, Lee perceived. The older woman was so genuine in her affectionate appraisal, it would have taken a harder heart than Lee possessed to give any hint that might destroy her illusions. Aloud, she offered, 'It came as a surprise to me, too.'

'What surprised you, darling?'

Lee heard that deep drawling query and turned slowly to see Marc strolling towards them. The endearment rankled, and it showed in the sparkling gaze she cast him. 'Your proposal,' she answered with a light smile that began and ended with the movement of her lips.

'Hm,' he began musingly, coming to stand close beside her. 'I thought I'd been most persuasive.'

'Oh, you were,' she agreed with droll vivacity, and he gave a husky laugh.

'However, you didn't imagine my intentions were honourable,' he slanted with amused cynicism, and Mrs Leone's eyes lit impishly alive.

'You have to allow you have an impressive track record,' she teased. 'Lee can't be blamed for thinking otherwise.'

'Dear Lord!' Marc raised his eyes heavenward. 'Do the two of you intend taking sides against me? I need a drink to bolster my morale.' His amused chuckle did strange things to Lee's composure, and she was forced to suffer his arm about her waist as they moved through to the lounge.

Champagne was fetched, and a touching toast to their future happiness demanded all Lee's acting ability as Marc linked his arm through hers and drank first from his glass then from hers, silently demanding that she do the same.

'I'll just pop through to the kitchen and prepare something for dinner,' Mrs Leone declared, rising to her feet. 'Steak and salad, I think, followed by fresh fruit.'

'I'll come and help,' Lee said quickly, but Marc's mother laughingly shook her head.

'Much as I'd love your company, Lee,' she refused, 'I'm sure Marc will appreciate it more.' Her smile was warm and slightly audacious as she glanced from one to the other. 'Fifteen minutes—I'll give you a call.'

'You haven't finished your champagne,' Marc drawled as the silence between them grew, and Lee shot him a level look.

'The reason for drinking it doesn't exactly enthrall me,' she declared evenly, and glimpsed his cynical amusement.

'I have you very much at my mercy, eh?' he slanted, and her eyes widened measurably as he extracted her glass from her nerveless fingers. Indolently watching her reaction, he deliberately lifted the rim to his mouth, taking care to select the part where she had placed her lips only minutes before.

'Do you have to behave so blatantly?' she demanded fiercely, and his eyes gleamed with silent laughter.

'What do you think of my *mamma*?' he parried mockingly, and Lee swallowed her anger with difficulty.

'She's nice,' she declared with complete sincerity.

'Quite the opposite of her son, in fact?'

'Totally,' she agreed with succinct sarcasm.

He replaced the glass down on to a nearby coffee table, then caught hold of her hand and pulled her close, winding his arms round her slim form, his expression lazily mocking.

'Don't, Marc,' Lee pleaded desperately as he lowered his head down to hers.

'Are you begging?' Marc taunted softly, his mouth bare inches above her own.

'Please.' The single word left her lips as an imploring whisper, and she pushed against his shoulders in an attempt to put some distance between them. 'Your mother——'

'Oh, Lee,' he chided softly, his eyes wicked as he brushed his lips over her temple. 'That's the very reason she left us alone. Mamma fondly imagines that being so newly engaged we can hardly manage to keep our hands off each other.' His vibrant glance roved intimately over her expressive features. 'The very least we can do is to give her reason to suspect you've been very thoroughly kissed in her absence.'

'It's not fair!' she cried, unbearably provoked, and he laughed.

'Why? Because you can't retaliate?'

'Yes—damn you!'

'Relax,' Marc bade pitilessly. 'You might find you enjoy it.'

'That would be impossible!'

His eyes hardened fractionally. 'Shall I prove just how wrong you are?'

Lee felt her stomach tighten painfully at the hidden threat, and she moved her head in an attempt to evade what she envisaged to be a brutal assault.

Hard fingers slid with careless disregard through her hair to hold fast her head, then his mouth closed over hers, blotting out everything save the taste of his kiss and the evocative seducing quality as his lips staked their possession.

Lee thought she had experienced every innovation in the numerous times he had kissed her, but she was mistaken. This time there was a savage sweetness that almost made her want to cry. Part of her wanted to believe the magic his touch evoked was more than mere sensual mastery, and the other part slowly died in the knowledge that it was deliberate. By his own admission he wanted her to appear bemused, generating an aura of dreamy enchantment for his mother's benefit.

Dinner was a friendly and intimate family meal during which Mrs Leone sought to fill in whatever gaps her son had left out in Lee's life style. There were moments when Lee was aware of Marc's slanting gaze as she conversed with his mother, and it took all her effort to direct him an occasional warm smile.

When the dishes had been dispensed with they had coffee in the lounge, then as soon as she could do so Lee excused herself on the pretext of a headache and indicated that she wished to leave.

'My dear, you should have mentioned it before,' Mrs Leone said with concern. 'Marc will take you home, and I'm sure a good night's rest will help.' Her face creased into a warm smile. 'I'll look forward to seeing you tomorrow evening. The barbecue,' she enlightened gently, and Lee said quickly,

'Yes, of course. Is there anything I can do? Perhaps I could come over in the afternoon and help with preparations.'

'Enjoy being a guest, Lee,' Marc's mother twinkled irrepressibly. 'It will probably be the last time. Besides, I have a bevy of relatives and friends who will each bring something. There's really only salads to prepare. The men take care of cooking the meat outdoors.'

With a smile Lee made her farewells, and conscious of Marc immediately behind she stepped down the path towards the gate. Once they were out of earshot she offered quietly, 'There's no need for you to take me in the car. It's not far, I'll walk.'

His negligent shrug was unrevealing. 'Whatever you want. But not alone, Lee,' he drawled, and her response was swift and bore traces of barely-concealed anger.

'Of course—forgive me. You must play the part of an adoring fiancée. In that case, I elect the car. It will mean less time spent in your company.'

His mocking salute as he held open the door was almost enough to make her scream, and in the few minutes it took to reach Alicia and Stefano's farm she didn't utter a single word.

'You're a spitting bundle of fury,' Marc commented cynically as he switched off the ignition, and leaning an arm on the steering wheel he turned towards her. 'I gather I'm the cause?'

'Who else?'

Reaching out a hand, he tilted her chin and glimpsed her sparkling gaze. 'Poor little girl,' he chided mockingly, and bending his head he brought his mouth close to hers, successfully stilling her struggles as she fought to evade him.

Lee's voice rose slightly in desperation. 'Don't,' she begged. 'I couldn't bear it.'

'Not kiss you?' Marc drawled, seeking the delicate hollow beneath a sensitive earlobe with his lips. 'Oh, but I shall—whenever and wherever I please.'

'I hate you,' Lee whispered against his mouth the instant before it closed over hers, and she was powerless to halt its ravaging possession.

It seemed an age before he disentangled her arms from about his neck and moved away. Lee felt emotionally drained, too enervated to do more than look at him through stricken eyes that mirrored her inner feelings far too readily.

'I love the way you hate,' Marc murmured as he trailed a gentle forefinger over her lips, tracing the outline of her mouth before moving over a cheekbone to push back a swathe of her hair that had fallen forward, partially covering her face. 'Go inside, Lee,' he bade quietly. 'I'll see you tomorrow, about six.'

She managed a strangled response as she reached blindly for the door clasp, then she was out of the car and almost running towards the verandah bordering the front of the house, and she didn't look back once.

CHAPTER SEVEN

'YOU'RE very quiet.'

Lee turned slightly and met Marc's faintly mocking gaze. 'I'm tired,' she declared equably, and saw his mouth curve into a lazy smile.

They were standing together in the floodlit gardens adjoining the house, surrounded by groups of talking, laughing guests intent on enjoying themselves. Music flowed from strategically mounted speakers, providing a pleasant background to what was undoubtedly a splendid party. It was difficult to judge the number present, but Lee calculated a hundred as a conservative estimate. News of the engagement had spread

like wildfire, so that the announcement part-way through
the evening had come as no surprise to anyone.

The array of food was nothing short of magnificent,
comprising tender young lamb roasted on a revolving
spit, chickens, pizzas, a variety of salad greens, garlic-
buttered bread rolls, as well as the traditional bar-
becued steaks and peppered pork sausages. Elaborate
cakes and a large bowl of fresh fruit salad comprised
dessert, and liquid refreshments consisted of casked
wine, beer and a variety of spirits.

'Let's dance.' It wasn't a suggestion, it was a command, and Lee tried to instil some warmth into her
smile as she moved across the lawn with Marc.

Several couples were swaying together in time to the
music, and with a sigh she permitted herself to be enfolded close against Marc's hard frame. She rested her
head against his chest and felt his breath stir her hair
as his lips brushed across the top of her head. A
strange lethargy crept into her limbs, and she controlled the faint shivering sensation that threatened to
shake her body. There was a certain danger in relaxing
her guard, for it would be all too easy to enjoy the
heady delight of being held in Marc's arms. Lulled by
a quantity of good food and a surfeit of wine, Lee cast
caution to the winds as she slowly lifted her arms and
clasped her hands round his neck. Idly she let her fingers trail through the hair that grew low on his nape as
her body moved sinuously with his in time to the
music. The subtle change in his hold as he arched her
even closer made her shockingly aware of him in a way
that left her in no doubt of his arousal.

Lee felt her senses begin to flare alive as his lips
trailed over her hair to her temple, then hovered close
to her ear.

'Damn all these people,' Marc cursed huskily. 'I'd like to have you all to myself—preferably in bed.'

Slowly she disentangled her arms from around his neck and let them slide down his chest. The effort it cost her to lift her head and meet his dark gleaming gaze was almost more than she could manage. 'That's one place I'll never be,' she said evenly, although there was nothing even about her rapid pulse-beat. The mere thought of that hard muscular body divested of clothing lying next to hers created an evocative enough image without pursuing the intimacies he would demand.

With studied indolence he let his eyes rove over her face, lingering at the tiny pulse that throbbed near her temple, then allowed it to slide slowly down to the edge of her mouth. 'Liar,' he accused softly. 'You want to be there almost as much as I need you there.'

'Need—want,' she choked. 'Why wrap it up? It all comes down to lust—sheer physical assuagement.' Goaded beyond endurance, she couldn't help adding, 'If you think that by having a ring put on my finger I'll let you—use me, then you're mistaken!' She felt the ache of unshed tears and pushed against his chest in an attempt to put some distance between them.

'Stop acting as if I were about to rape you,' Marc drawled, and she gave a mirthless laugh.

'Oh, you're much too subtle for that. You possess a master's degree in sensual expertise,' she accorded bitterly. 'What is it about me that attracts you, Marc? Do I present a challenge because I don't grovel for your attention?' She cast her eyes wildly over the guests. 'Have you looked at the women here tonight? Half of them envy me, but it's the other half I worry about.

Given the slightest chance they'd scratch my eyes out!'

'You're becoming hysterical, and without cause.' His gaze hardened fractionally as he raked her features.

'How can you say that?'

'What do you want to hear? That I've lived the life of a monk?' he demanded dryly. 'I have a healthy sexual appetite, and I won't deny there have been several women in my life.' His lips curved to form a mocking smile as he drew her close. 'Remember my so-called exalted place in the community,' he taunted. 'All these young women you're referring to come from respectable families, with staunchly protective fathers,' he added with wry cynicism. 'Harm so much as a hair of their daughters' heads, and I'd be hounded by a posse of rifle-toting *papas*.'

Lee didn't bother to comment, and she would have given anything to simply turn and walk away. From Marc Leone, the party—the whole town.

'Let's rejoin some of the guests,' Marc suggested tolerantly, and stepping back a pace he let his arm fall over her shoulders as he turned her towards the house.

To everyone present they must have appeared an ideal couple, Lee thought wryly. Certainly throughout what remained of the evening Marc rarely left her side, and his attentiveness couldn't be faulted. There was no chance of her being left alone to parry the barely-concealed animosity engendered by Daniella and Marita. That would come later, when they had the opportunity to get her alone. The threat was there, nonetheless, and Lee felt almost inclined to challenge both girls to pistols at dawn.

The guest of honour, Carlo Morelli, was a charming man in his mid-thirties who had little difficulty fitting into the easy friendship he had previously shared with everyone present. His regard for Marc was apparent, and he made no secret of the fact that he found Lee utterly captivating.

'Trust Marc to claim you first,' Carlo declared, his attractive features assuming an expression of mock-regret. 'If only I had come home sooner, I'd have wooed you away from him.'

'Not a chance, my friend,' Marc told him with a dry smile, and Lee tilted her head slightly in teasing speculation.

'He's a very persuasive man, Carlo. I've scarcely had a moment to think straight since we first met.'

The other man's laughter held genuine amusement. 'A force to be reckoned with, eh?' He glanced towards Marc and indicated the guests with an encompassing gesture. 'I guess the next occasion we all get together will be for your wedding. Have you set a date yet?'

Lee opened her mouth to protest, only to hear Marc say blandly,

'Soon. There are a few minor details to work out.'

'At the risk of a refusal, what say we make up a party and drive to Atherton for dinner one night this week?' His smile became faintly mocking. 'Or do you want to be alone?'

'I'd like that,' Lee said quickly, and glancing up at Marc she gave him a beguiling smile. 'What do you think, darling?'

His answering smile held indolent amusement. 'Why not?' he agreed. 'Shall we say Thursday?'

'Excellent. I'll ring you tomorrow and we'll arrange the details.'

'Not tomorrow,' Marc declined. 'Lee and I are taking a day trip over to Green Island. We'll fit in with whatever arrangements you make for Thursday evening, and meet you inside the restaurant around seven.'

'Why did you tell Carlo we're getting married soon?' Lee demanded in an undertone the instant they were out of earshot.

'What did you expect me to say?' Marc slanted her a dark gleaming glance that held amused cynicism. 'That I have a fiancée who has no intention of attending her own wedding?'

'But why *soon*?' she insisted with a frown. 'You could have hinted that it might take place towards the end of the year.'

'At the height of the tobacco season?' he queried. 'Six months from now?' He gave a deep throaty chuckle. 'They'd question my restraint.'

'What about me?' she queried in a furious whisper. 'I hardly know you. Surely I should be given time to remedy that?'

'Why get so angry over something you insist will never happen?' Marc countered smoothly, and she clenched her teeth against the tirade she longed to heap upon his arrogant head.

'Because I hate the idea of everyone thinking I can't wait to marry you,' she flung furiously. 'According to gossip, you're the catch of the decade, and I can only be interested in your money!'

His gaze was disconcertingly level. 'But you are—by your own admission. Remember?'

Dear God, how could she forget those foolishly goaded words about only marrying a millionaire? Except the bluff had backfired, and with every day that passed she found herself getting deeper and deeper into the mire.

'I hate deceiving everyone,' Lee said wretchedly. 'My sister—your mother. It isn't fair!'

'If you continue to frown, it will be imagined we're about to have our first fight,' Marc drawled, and she stifled a bitter laugh.

'That's all we ever do—fight, *argue*! We can't agree on anything!'

'Oh, I can think of several occasions when we've been in perfect accord,' he said musingly, and it was all she could do not to hit him.

'Stop it, Marc. Otherwise I'll walk out of here,' she threatened emotively.

'Be warned I'd follow you,' he drawled in a voice that was dangerously quiet. 'And there would be no doubt about the outcome.'

'You couldn't leave your guests,' Lee flung with a bravery she didn't feel. 'What would they think?'

His negligent shrug was uncaring. 'I don't need to explain my actions to anyone. As to what they might think—I imagine they would draw their own conclusions.'

'You really don't care, do you?' she choked. 'You're a hard, unfeeling brute!'

'I haven't achieved success by being negative,' Marc told her hardily, and she felt sickened by his inflexibility.

'No,' she agreed slowly. 'You size up your objective, choose a course of action, then sweep aside everything that stands in your way. Maybe one day you'll come up against someone who'll refuse to give in. The one thing I regret is that I won't be around to see your downfall.'

'You make me sound like a satanic monster,' he inclined mockingly.

'You play by your own rules, Marc. Maybe it's time you revised them.'

On previous occasions when Lee had travelled north for her holidays something had always transpired to prevent a trip to Green Island, and she couldn't help the feeling of anticipation as the launch left Cairns early on Wednesday morning and headed out towards the small tropical isle.

In a strapless sun-frock of jade towelling material that showed off her cream-textured skin to advantage, she presented an attractive figure as she gazed out over the spume of sea water spreading from the stern. A light breeze teased the length of her hair, lifting and ruffling it into disarray, and she turned slightly as she felt a hand brush a stray lock back behind her ear.

'I should have brought a scarf,' Lee grinned ruefully, and was unable to prevent the faint quickening of her heartbeat as she caught Marc's answering smile. He looked incredibly fit in dark shorts and a black short-sleeved shirt left unbuttoned almost to the waist.

'You suit the casual windblown look,' he remarked with lazy mockery, and she wrinkled her nose at him.

'Am I meant to take that as a compliment?'

'Are you fishing for one?'

'No, of course not,' Lee said evenly, unaccountably hurt that he should think her deliberately provocative. She swallowed convulsively and turned her gaze back out over the ocean. Marc had the power to wound in a way she had thought was impossible, for no man had ever made her feel so vulnerable or so emotionally at odds. As it was, he was constantly in her thoughts. If she wasn't careful she'd join the multitude of women who had fallen hoplessly in love with him, and that would never do.

She gave a sudden start as she felt his hand curve over her shoulder and trail to her nape. More than anything she wanted to beg him to stop the subtle torture his touch evoked, but doubtless he would be amused and that would be more than she could bear. The only defence she had was anger, but self-respect and a modicum of good manners forbade her to resort to such a display in the presence of others.

'You're trembling,' Marc asserted quietly, and it took considerable effort for her to turn and smile.

'Am I? I can't think why.' She cast her gaze back towards the rapidly disappearing coastline. 'The hills are very dark against the skyline, aren't they?'

'They form part of the Great Dividing Range,' Marc informed her, and she missed the sudden gleam that appeared in his dark eyes.

Lee was supremely conscious of his fingers effecting an evocative massage beneath the heavy swathe of her hair, and more than anything she wanted to feel the touch of his mouth on hers. It was crazy, but right at that moment she was oblivious to everything but the desire to be close against him. Nothing else mattered, and the knowledge that he had the power to render her so malleable made her angry. In fact, it was almost funny when she could see the humour of the situation. Here she was engaged to the man and to all intents and purposes supposedly enraptured at the thought of marrying him, yet inside she was an emotional wreck torn between the desires that flamed her body and the rational logical part of her mind that upheld her moral inhibitions.

After a lengthy silence she said the first thing that came into her head. 'How long have you known Carlo?'

'All my life. We went to school together, then on to college and university,' Marc revealed, moving his arm to rest across her shoulders.

'Where has he been these past few years?'

'Genuine interest, Lee?' he taunted softly. 'Or merely a conversational gambit?'

She swallowed the sudden lump that rose in her throat. 'Both. We can hardly spend the entire day without talking, and we've exhausted my life and yours. Besides,' she said with sudden anger, 'he reminds me of you—he projects unenviable cynicism.'

His soft chuckle did little to ease her ruffled composure. 'Really? Is that how you see me—as a confirmed cynic?' His mouth moved to form a wry smile. 'Perhaps I am. As for Carlo, he's had rather a hard time of it. His wife died a few months ago of cancer.'

Lee's features softened with genuine sympathy. 'How sad,' she said quietly, and her eyes widened slightly as Marc lifted a hand to touch her cheek.

'Life is sad,' he opined with a touch of mockery. 'We all struggle for survival, one way or another. It's part of our existence.'

'Tell me something about Green Island,' she said a trifle desperately, and he smiled, his dark eyes agleam with hidden amusement.

'We'll arrive there soon, then you'll be free of our fellow passengers. I imagine the instant we're alone you'll become your usual self. Having to guard your tongue is proving something of a strain!'

His silent laughter was almost the very limit, and she didn't bother to speak so much as a word until the launch reached the wharf at Green Island.

Lee felt as if she had been transported into a tropical paradise as she stepped on the Island's sandy shore, for evident were an abundance of pandanus trees, their wide-spreading palms providing shade and a welcoming coolness. Holiday cabins lent a carefree atmosphere, and there was a well-equipped shop and restaurant to cater to the guests' needs. Bright music was emitted from concealed speakers, mingling with the laughter and noise, and it was impossible not to catch the mood the organisers endeavoured to project.

'It's like another world,' Lee commented, and the smile she cast Marc wasn't contrived.

'Shall we declare a truce?'

This time she didn't take offence at his mocking amusement, and tucking an arm through his she broke into an irrepressible grin. 'We can but try. Who knows? We might surprise ourselves!'

His mouth curved into a relaxed smile as he gazed down at her. 'What do you want to do first?'

'You mean to say I get to choose?'

'Oh, I think I can allow you that consideration,' he drawled, and she wrinkled her nose at him.

'Well, after two hours on the launch, I vote we undertake some exercise. Can we walk around the Island?'

'Why not?'

'Then lunch,' Lee elected. 'A swim, and an hour or two sunbathing. What time does the launch return to Cairns?'

'Three o'clock.'

'Lovely,' she declared, feeling suddenly carefree. Today would be special, she felt it in her bones. Besides, when Marc set out to be charming he could melt her animosity into insignificance.

During their stroll along the sandy shore, Lee

paused constantly in search of shells, although an undamaged conch was a rare find owing to the Island being almost totally surrounded by a coral reef. The sun's warmth caressed her skin, and when they had come full circle she pushed fingers through her hair in an endeavour to restore some order to its tumbled tresses.

'You look beautiful,' Marc told her softly, and his smile did crazy things to her equilibrium. 'Let's eat, shall we?'

The restaurant was larger than Lee expected, and her appetite was sharpened by the fresh sea air, so that she ate heartily of the mixed seafood dish that was placed before her, and washed down with a light white wine it was one of the finest meals she had tasted in a long while.

'I feel incredibly lazy,' Lee groaned as they wandered along the path leading down to the beach, and Marc gave a husky chuckle.

'Serves you right,' he declared, showing no sympathy at all. 'You won't be able to swim for at least an hour.'

'I intend stretching out on my towel, and I shall probably fall asleep,' she said, sliding her sunglasses down from their resting place on top of her head. 'What do you have planned?'

His slanting mockery set the butterflies in her stomach turning wild somersaults, and she was glad of the darkened protective lenses shading her eyes. 'Oh, I shall stand guard, I think,' he said lazily. 'If I disappear into the bar you'll have to fight off a few admirers,' he finished dryly, and she glanced at him with a frown. 'Don't tell me you haven't noticed?' he queried cynically.

'I was too busy admiring the scenery,' she said

honestly, and he laughed.

'You're a very eye-catching piece of scenery your-self,' he declared wryly, and she pulled a face at him.

'Maybe I should check the female population,' she felt inclined to tease. 'You tend to radiate a certain masculine charisma all your own.'

'Is that an admission?'

'I don't intend inflating your ego. You're impossible enough as it is!'

'Cheeky little thing, aren't you?' Marc drawled. 'I wonder if you would dare to be so impudent if we were alone.'

'Don't spoil it,' Lee begged quietly. 'I hate it when you become cynical.' She reached into her beachbag and extracted a large towel which she quickly spread out on the sand, then beneath his steadfast gaze she stripped off the strapless frock to reveal a bikini in jade silk stretch fabric. Retrieving the straps of the halter-top, she tied them round her neck, then slid gracefully down to lie full length on her towel.

Seconds later she gave a startled gasp as a blob of cold cream landed between her shoulder-blades, and she lifted her head and swung round to face him.

'You'll burn,' Marc explained dryly. 'Relax, and I'll apply some sunscreen cream.'

Relax? He had to be joking! Lee closed her eyes and tried to ignore the swift gnawing ache that took over the lower region of her stomach as his hands began a soothing massage that didn't stop at her shoulders. Lightly they moved down towards her waist, then curved lower over the gentle swell of her hips. When he began on the backs of her thighs she was almost at screaming point.

'When you're ready to turn over, I'll complete the task.'

'I can manage to do the front myself,' she declared in a muffled voice, and heard his husky laughter.

'Pity,' he drawled. 'That's something I was looking forward to.'

Lee turned her head away from him, and was grateful for the curtain of hair that partially concealed her face. She was aware of the faint rustle of clothing and surmised he was shedding his shorts and shirt to take advantage of the sun.

Lulled by the quantity of food and wine she had consumed, Lee dozed for a while, then stirred and rolled over on to her back, blinking slightly as a shadow loomed across her slim curves.

'Stay still,' Marc commanded softly, and her eyes widened as they focused on him

Clothes had hinted at his physical fitness, but now devoid of any apparel except the brief black swimming trunks that hugged his hips, he presented an awe-inspiring figure. Tanned skin covered tightly-muscled sinew, displaying a raw virility that made her catch her breath.

Lee felt the massaging touch of his fingers on her midriff and she tried to remain blasé when they slid down over her stomach. Then slowly she felt them move to her throat, and she unconsciously held her breath as they moved down towards the swell of her breasts.

The next instant she gave a soundless cry as his fingers slid the silky material aside to expose the creamy fullness beneath, then she gave a shocked gasp as he lowered his mouth to one delicate rosy tip. His touch sent a wild spiral of sensation sweeping through her body, and in one lurching movement she pushed his head aside as she struggled to sit up. Incredible anger lent her strength, and within seconds she was free and on to her feet as she strove to control her ragged breathing. About to run, she felt her hand caught in a merciless grip, then the next instant she was pulled down beside him.

'Don't look so offended,' Marc said bluntly, and when she refused to look at him he placed a hand beneath her chin and tilted it so that she had no choice. 'No one witnessed it, and even if they had, it isn't so very terrible.'

'Let me go,' she said shakily, unable to meet those dark eyes.

'Would you rather I'd kissed you?'

A slow blush tinged her cheeks. 'I don't like public displays of—passion,' she explained, and felt her lips tremble as his eyes roved over her face with lazy mockery.

'My dear Lee,' Marc said softly, his teeth gleaming white as his lips parted in a cynical smile, 'you haven't experienced my passion. So far, I've behaved with gentlemanly restraint.'

His amusement was the last straw, and with an inarticulate cry she broke away from him, then shakily discarding her sunglasses she slid to her feet and ran down to the water's edge. Tears shimmered, blurring her vision, and she blinked rapidly in an effort to dispel them.

The coolness of the sea acted like a balm to her tortured nerves, and she sank beneath its surface, then emerged to swim strongly away from the shallows. If it were possible she would have liked to swim out of sight of the wharf, but these were tropic waters in which several breaks in the coral reef allowed free passage of the ever-prevalent danger of sharks.

It was all of thirty minutes before she returned to

shore, and she was conscious of Marc's intent scrutiny as she moved towards him.

'I was just about to come and get you,' he drawled as she reached for her towel, and his eyes sharpened as they fell to the thin trickle of blood seeping from her foot. 'Did you scrape against some coral?'

Lee patted herself dry, then spread out the towel and sat down. With a careless shrug she glanced down at her foot. 'I don't remember. It could have been a shell.' She reached forward and dabbed at the graze with the edge of her towel, feeling it sting for the first time.

'Little fool,' Marc said brusquely as he leaned towards her. 'A coral graze can easily become infected. Let me see it.' He took her foot between his hands and examined it carefully, then her breath caught in her throat as he bent down and placed his mouth to the wound.

'What are you doing?' Her voice came out as a scandalised gasp, and she couldn't help the faint shuddering sensation that ran through her body as he sucked hard against her flesh.

'There, that should help. I've some antibiotic cream at home that will prevent any infection,' he told her smoothly.

'It seems an awful fuss to make over a small graze.' She met his gaze with difficulty, and discovered it was impossible to read his expression.

'You'll do as I suggest,' he declared evenly. 'Go and get changed. The launch leaves in an hour, and we've yet to visit the underwater observatory.'

Lee gave a rueful grimace as she smoothed back her wet hair. 'I think I'll take a shower in the changing shed. If I don't get the salt out of my hair, it will dry into an uncontrollable mess.' Catching up her beach-bag, she rose to her feet and headed towards the pandanus trees without so much as a backward glance.

Ten minutes later she emerged feeling cool and re-freshed, and with her sunglasses in place she strolled towards the wharf where Marc stood waiting. Together they walked along the long jetty towards the underwater observatory, and there Lee was exposed to a wonderland of exotic colour as many species of tropical fish were revealed in all their natural splendour.

Several other visitors crowded the narrow walkways, and Lee was supremely conscious of Marc's presence. More than once she brushed against him, and the touch of his arm as it rested about her waist brought a warmth tingling through her veins that was beyond her control.

The return trip seemed to take no time at all, and on reaching Cairns Lee followed Marc to the car, slipping into the front seat with a sigh of pleasure that wasn't contrived.

'Thank you for a lovely day.'

His smile was without mockery as he leaned forward to switch on the ignition. 'Very politely said,' he slanted musingly. 'Let's head somewhere for a few drinks before dinner.'

'Dinner? But I'm not dressed to eat out,' Lee protested, and coloured slightly as his gaze roved over her in an indolent intimate appraisal.

'You look fine to me. In fact,' he opined provokingly, 'knowing precisely what you're *not* wearing beneath that sun-frock is enough to make me want to forgo food in favour of *you*.'

'I'd prefer to go home, if you don't mind,' she managed quietly. 'I've had a succession of late nights recently, and we're dining out again tomorrow evening.'

'I do mind. However, I intend delivering you safely home before ten,' Marc informed her, and with competent ease he slid the large Fairlane out into the moving stream of traffic.

'No arguments?' he taunted several minutes later when he had parked the car outside a hotel, and Lee gave a slight shrug.

'What's the use? You don't take any notice of them.'

Marc directed her a long hard glance, then his lips curved into a lazy smile. 'Poor Lee! I'm not entirely the brute you think me. Let's have a drink, then we'll eat. I fancy pasta—how about you? After coffee, we'll head home, I promise.

'*Lasagna al forno?*'

His faint chuckle brought forth an answering smile. 'Done.'

It was almost eight when they began ascending the Kuranda Range, and replete with good food and wine Lee lay her head back and closed her eyes.

'Hey, sleepyhead—wake up!' A deep voice invaded her dreams, and she struggled upright, rubbing her eyes as she tried to orientate herself with her surroundings.

'Are we home already?'

'We are—although mine, not yours,' Marc said musingly. 'I want to tend that foot first. If I'm not mistaken, you'll fall into bed having forgotten all about it.'

'It doesn't even hurt,' she protested as she followed him indoors, and she sat quiescent as he bathed and dressed the wound.

'All right, Sleeping Beauty,' he smiled. 'Now I'll see you into bed.'

Lee felt her eyes widen into enormous pools, then became shuttered as she glimpsed his amusement. The next instant she was swept up into his arms and he carried her out to the car as if she weighed little more than a child.

'Goodnight, little girl,' Marc taunted softly the moment he brought the car to a halt in Stefano's driveway.

Lee gazed at him in bemusement, her lips soft and tremulous as his mouth settled briefly on hers.

'I'll collect you around six tomorrow evening,' he told her, leaning across to open her door. 'Sweet dreams, *cara*.'

CHAPTER EIGHT

'WE'RE the first to arrive,' Lee declared as she slipped into the chair Marc held out for her. 'Do you know who is coming with Carlo?'

'The Conti sisters, I believe,' he revealed wryly, and Lee experienced a vague feeling of unease.

'Daniella and Marita?'

'Both,' said Marc with a slight smile. 'I imagine John will make up a reluctant fourth.'

Attired in formal clothes, he exuded a sophistication she found a trifle frightening. There was an air of leashed strength that was compelling, an intensity that hadn't been apparent the previous day.

Lee had dressed carefully, choosing a simple strap-less dress in white silk whose skirt was pencil-slim and split almost to mid-thigh on one side, the bodice drap-ing over her bosom in a soft blouson style from a narrow gathered band. Slender high-heeled shoes with thin shoestring straps curving round the back of her heels and across her toes added an elegance that was enhanced by the addition of a delicate lacy shawl. Apart from the magnificent diamond adorning her left hand she wore a slim gold chain at her neck and a matching bracelet at her wrist. Her make-up was understated, except for eyeshadow and mascara that highlighted her eyes, and a bold red outlined the gener-ous curves of her mouth.

'What would you like to drink?' Marc queried, and after a brief perusal of the wine list Lee decided she would prefer something light and fairly innocu-ous.

'Sauternes?' He gave the order to the hovering waiter, then settled back in his chair to regard her with thoughtful contemplation. 'I hope I'm the one you dressed to impress?' he slanted with faint mockery, and she met his gaze a shade defiantly.

'I brought mainly casual clothes with me,' she ex-plained. 'If I'd known I was embarking on a mad social whirl I would have packed something more suitable.'

Marc's mouth curved into a teasing smile. 'What you're wearing is guaranteed to have a devastating effect on the opposite sex,' he assured her sar-donically. 'I only hope Carlo and John can stand the strain.'

'And you, Marc? Or daren't I ask?'

His lips twitched with wry humour. 'I think you're aware of the effect you create.'

It was as well the waiter appeared at that moment with the wine, and after a few bracing sips Lee felt ready to deal with whatever the evening would bring.

'Here they are now,' Marc murmured, and she glanced across the room to see Daniella and Marita being led towards them by Carlo and, as Marc had predicted, John.

'You beat us to it, I see,' Carlo declared on reaching them, and Marc directed a lazy encompassing smile.

'Only by a matter of five minutes.'

Lee forced a measure of enthusiasm into her voice as she greeted the two Conti sisters, only to have it returned in a bright superficial manner. Both girls were elegantly attired in the latest fashion, and their make-up was flawless. Daniella had opted for a figure-hugging black dress that clung to her generous curves in a way that left nothing to the imagination, and Marita had chosen a more tailored look in deep cream linen.

After consuming the first course Lee sat back and lifted her wine-glass, savouring the contents with enjoyment.

'You're very quiet tonight,' John commented, leaning close, and she turned with a faint smile.

'I don't mean to be,' she said lightly, and she caught Carlo's chuckling amusement as he leaned across the table.

'What were you dreaming of, Lee? Wedding gowns and intended honeymoon destinations?'

A slight tinge of pink crept up to her cheeks that wasn't helped when Daniella entered into the conversation with barely-concealed pique.

'Have you set the date yet, Marc?'

'The first Saturday in June,' he said sardonically, his eyes brilliant as he dared Lee to deny it, and she kept the faint smile in place with difficulty as Marita exclaimed,

'But that's only three weeks!'

'What's the rush? We imagined the wedding to be months away,' Daniella declared, and her eyes swept over Lee with barely concealed insolence.

'Indeed?' Marc drawled, then turning to Lee he directed her a warm smile. 'More wine, darling?'

'Thank you.' So she did possess a voice, after all! For a few crazy moments Lee thought it had deserted her. She felt so shaky, she doubted she could lift the glass to her lips without spilling its contents, and she sat in silence, too stunned to offer anything by way of conversation.

'I'd like to dance with your beautiful fiancée,' Carlo intimated to Marc. 'You don't mind?' His eyes bore a silent challenge, and Marc met his gaze with a startlingly measured look.

'You will have to ask Lee.'

Carlo's smile became vaguely sardonic as he transferred his attention. 'Well, Lee? Could you bear to dance with me, do you think?'

Put like that, how could she refuse? Lee stood to her feet, removed her shawl and placed it over the back of her chair, then allowed him to lead her towards the small dance floor.

'Thank you,' she said quietly as she slipped into his arms, and he gave a wry smile.

'For rescuing you?'

'How did you guess?'

His slight smile held sympathy and a hint of pity. 'I happened to be looking at you when Marc dropped his bombshell,' he said dryly. 'Am I right in supposing it was a total surprise?'

Her monosyllabic confirmation made him grimace.

'I can't say I blame him. Given a similar opportunity, I'd do exactly the same.'

'I beg your pardon?' Lee asked, casting him a startled glance.

'Oh, Lee,' he chastised mockingly, 'don't you ever look in a mirror?'

'Several times a day, every day of my life,' she responded cynically, and he laughed with genuine amusement.

'And what you see is so familiar, you're beyond analytical judgment, hm?'

'There's always something about ourselves we'd like to change,' she imparted with unexpected wisdom, and Carlo's expression softened.

'Just what would you like to change, for heaven's sake?'

'My temper.' The choice was unequivocal, and he gave a subdued chuckle.

'So you possess a temper.' Carlo shook his head slightly, and his expression assumed mocking amusement. 'You argue with Marc?'

'Incessantly.'

'After a surfeit of women who fall over themselves to please him, you undoubtedly act like a breath of fresh air,' he said drolly, and she directed him a mischievous grin.

'More like a gale, I'd say!'

'Do you love him?'

The query shocked her into silence for several

minutes, then she ventured carefully, 'What makes you ask that?'

'Because I think you're afraid of him.'

'A little healthy awe, perhaps,' she said lightly. 'But hardly fear.'

'No?' His dark eyes were far too perceptive as they raked her mobile features. 'You lack the glow of a woman who has known a lover. I rather think you're what's known as a sweet old-fashioned girl.'

Lee swallowed, then managed a smile. 'I think we should get back to the others.'

Carlo laughed out loud. 'How adroit,' he said musingly. 'Are you imagining Marc may be jealous?'

'I don't think so,' she said evenly.

'Daniella and Marita never stood a chance, my dear,' he told her dryly, and she gave a slight start in confusion. 'Don't misconstrue the friendship. It goes back a long way, and you have my word that Marc's interest has never been other than brotherly.' Releasing his hold, he turned and led her back to their table, and as soon as she was seated she reached for her glass, needing the slight boost the alcohol would provide.

During the main course Daniella took pleasure in returning to the subject of the proposed wedding, and her interest extended far beyond the bounds of casual contemplation.

'Have you chosen your gown yet, Lee? White is a little too——' she paused delicately, 'insipid, with your colouring. Cream would be far more flattering.'

'Yards of lace,' Marita insisted. 'And a long veil. Your hair will have to be professionally styled.' Her scrutiny was hardly kind. 'Have you tried wearing it up?'

'I thought of wearing satin,' Lee declared with evident seriousness, although anyone who knew her well would have seen the danger signs in the way her eyes deepened to a clear brilliant topaz. 'Perfectly plain, and a picture hat—no veil. And,' she added for good measure, 'I insist on roses for a bridal bouquet.'

Carlo's eyes lit with hidden laughter, although she didn't dare spare Marc a glance. Daniella looked decidedly put out, and Marita was seemingly intent on forking small fastidious mouthfuls of food into her mouth.

It wasn't until after they had finished dessert that Marc indicated Lee should dance with him, and it was on the tip of her tongue to refuse. After a momentary pause she rose to her feet, and her indecision brought a faint tightening of his mouth.

'A little more enthusiasm wouldn't go amiss.'

Lee glanced up and met his dark grey eyes, then deliberately looked away. 'You're insufferable,' she said conversationally. She even smiled for the benefit of anyone looking on. 'If you think by giving a date to our supposed wedding you can coerce me into marriage, then you're mistaken.'

'You positively sparkled in Carlo's arms,' Marc drawled, pulling her close against him. His hands were low on her back, moulding her to his long length with deceptive strength.

'Were you watching? Didn't Daniella and Marita provide sufficient distraction?' Her tongue was waspish, but she couldn't help it.

'If you don't behave, I'll——'

'What, Marc?' she demanded. 'I've been slapped, kissed senseless, and I've suffered bruises as evidence of your brutishness.' Her voice choked slightly. 'Perhaps I can be forgiven for asking what else you have in store for me?'

Without a word he released her, then taking hold of her hand he led the way back to their table and collected her shawl. His smile was a facsimile of polite civility as it encompassed the four people sitting at their table. 'If you'll excuse us? Carlo, John—please remain for the rest of the evening as my guests.' Turning slightly, he raised his hand and received immediate attention from a hawk-eyed waiter. When the bill was settled he inclined his head, then holding Lee's hand in an excruciating grip he made his way to the entrance.

Outside, she attempted to wrench herself out of his grasp, and her cry of pain was very real. 'Marc—you're hurting me!'

'Not half as much as I'd like to,' he muttered emotively.

'Oh, this is impossible!' She tugged at the ring on her finger, only to sag forward against him in pain as he tightened his grip.

'Take that off, and I won't be responsible for my actions.'

Tears welled up behind her eyes, clouding her vision, and she said shakily, 'Let me go, Marc.'

With a gesture of disgust he released her hand, and his eyes hardened as he watched her attempt to ease the severe bruising. Abruptly he reached forward and unlocked the car. 'Get in.'

The instant she was seated the door closed with a decisive snap, and she didn't offer so much as a word as he slid in behind the wheel. Part of her was terrified he would alleviate his anger by driving at breakneck speed, but minutes later she had to credit him with more control as he set the large vehicle moving along the highway.

Gradually Lee flexed her fingers, feeling them one by one and failing to find any lasting damage. Surreptitiously she withdrew a handkerchief and dabbed the gash her ring had caused, winding the soft linen square round her finger to stem the stickiness trickling down towards her palm. Slowly she eased her head back against the headrest and closed her eyes. If she didn't the tears would overflow, and to have Marc witness her crying would be untenable.

She wasn't conscious of the miles that brought them steadily closer to Mareeba, and as the car slacked speed and eased to a halt her hand automatically went to the door-clasp, only to falter as she became aware of her surroundings. There weren't any farm buildings in sight, only a density of trees within her peripheral vision. Slowly she swung round towards Marc, her gaze remarkably steady. 'Whatever you want to say, at least get it over with.'

'Words, Lee?' His harsh laugh was self-derisory, and she gazed sightlessly out the window.

The silence stretched between them until Lee could bear it no longer. 'Please take me home. I've no idea where we are, otherwise I'd get out and walk.'

'Do you imagine I'd let you?'

She lifted a hand in a gesture of helplessness, then let it drop down on to her lap. 'I really don't know,' she said shakily. 'I only know we can't go on like this.'

'I couldn't agree more,' Marc declared hardily.

Lee felt stifled by his presence, the explosive anger beneath the surface of his control, and she stared blindly out the windscreen as she fought off the stupid threat of ignominious tears.

When she felt a hand touch hers she couldn't help the audible gasp that left her lips. The next instant the interior light snapped on, and even as she pulled away Marc leaned forward and captured her wrist.

His husky string of oaths blistered her ears, and she pulled her hand away and shakily rewound the handkerchief.

'Don't touch me—I couldn't bear it,' she choked desperately, and the next instant her face was caught and she had no option but to look at him.

'Sweet Mother of God!' Marc muttered huskily as he glimpsed her stricken features. Without a word he released her seatbelt, flicked a lever that sent his seat moving back from the wheel, then reached out and lifted her on to his lap.

His gentleness was the last straw, and the tears overflowed to slip down her cheeks and soak his shirt. '*Dio*,' he cursed emotively. 'For the love of heaven, don't cry!'

'I'm not,' Lee denied shakily as she attempted to move away from him. Hardly aware of what she was doing she brushed wretchedly at her cheeks, then she heard him give a husky groan as his head lowered down to hers.

Gently he caught hold of her hands, then his lips moved over each cheek in turn before trailing down to close possessively over her mouth.

Lee withstood the seducing sensuality of his touch for as long as she could, then with a moan of despair she parted her lips to allow his hungry possession.

She had no awareness of time or place as he sought to bring alive the flame deep within, and she gave a silent gasp as she felt his hands slip the silky material of her dress down to expose her bosom.

'Sweet heaven, you're beautiful,' Marc groaned, lowering his head to the deep valley between each creamy breast. Gently he moved his mouth from one to the other, sending deep pleasurable sensations radiating wildly from every nerve.

Just as Lee thought she couldn't stand another second, he began a sensitive exploration of first one rosy peak before moving to the other, teasing until she moaned an entreaty to desist. Hardly aware of what she was doing, she undid the buttons on his shirt, and the feel of the dark springy hair against her fingertips evoked an irresistible desire to have her body touch his without any restrictive clothing.

'Marc—please——'

Hands caught hold of her shoulders and he gently pushed her away. 'The offer is very tempting, my sweet, and I must admit if I listened to my baser instincts I'd take advantage of you right here and now.' He leaned forward and planted a brief hard kiss on her trembling mouth. 'Instead, I'll take you home.' His brief laugh held bitter irony as he glanced at her state of déshabille. 'Then I'll go and take a cold shower.' Gently he caught hold of the bodice of her dress and pulled it up over her bosom, then with a harsh sigh he turned and switched on the ignition.

Lee slowly came down from the sensual plateau to cruel reality, and she closed her eyes as wave after wave of embarrassment flooded through her body. Dear God, she thought shakily, what had she done? How could she have had so little self-control? With a broken sob she covered her face with her hands. She had behaved like a shameless wanton in his arms, without thought of any consequences. If it hadn't been for Marc calling a halt to their lovemaking ... Oh God, it didn't bear thinking about.

'Lee—for heaven's sake,' Marc groaned as he brought the car to a halt in the driveway outside Stefano's house. 'Don't look so tragic. You've done nothing of which you should be ashamed.' He reached forward and caught hold of her chin, tilting it so she was forced to look at him.

'How can you say that?' she whispered in agonised disbelief.

'You're nothing but a babe,' he said with a slight smile, and traced her lips with an idle finger before reaching across and opening her door. 'Go inside like a good girl, and I'll see you tomorrow.'

Tomorrow? Lee knew she would never be able to face him again. 'Goodnight.' Was that her voice? It sounded so distant and far away. Without a backward glance she slid out from the car and ran up the path to the front door. Luckily Alicia and Stefano were already in bed, and with the movements of an automaton she carefully locked up and made her way down the hall to her room.

Slowly she cast off her clothes and slid between the sheets, to lie staring sightlessly up at the darkened ceiling until the first pink fingers of the new day's dawn crept over the horizon.

As Friday progressed, Lee became increasingly vague and introspective, incurring Alicia's speculative concern on more than one occasion. Twice Marc had phoned, but Lee refused to take either call, insisting Alicia should say she was busy outside with the children, or in the shower—any feasible excuse would do, just so long as she didn't have to speak to him.

'Have you and Marc had an argument?'

Lee concentrated on folding freshly laundered towelling squares into a neat pile and studiously avoided meeting her sister's discerning gaze. 'What makes you think that?'

'Oh, come on, Lee—this is Alicia, remember?'

If only it was something as simple as an argument! Torn between taking her sister into her confidence or settling for a half-truth, Lee decided on the latter. It was less complicated. 'I think Marc and I are seeing too much of each other,' she said pensively. 'Everything has happened so fast, I haven't even become accustomed to being engaged, let alone considering getting married.'

'He's decided on a date?'

Lee nodded, her features serious as she turned to meet her sister's expressive solicitude. 'The first Saturday in June,' she said, and her eyes clouded momentarily. 'I'd like to disappear,' she muttered with an earnestness that brought Alicia's eyebrows ascending high into her forehead.

'As bad as that? We'd better organise a plan of action, because unless I'm mistaken Marc will arrive on the doorstep—if not before dinner, then certainly after,' Alicia declared dryly, and Lee gave a wry grimace.

'Perhaps I could develop a migraine?'

'That, combined with the necessity for an early night. You could have a snack and miss dinner, just in case he comes while we're eating.'

Lee frowned slightly. 'Do you think it will work?'

'I doubt it,' Alicia responded matter-of-factly. 'Marc is no fool. If he suspects he's being given the runaround, he's just as likely to ignore everything I say.'

'Then I'd better make it look authentic,' Lee
determined, feeling slightly nonplussed at the
prospect.

At seven o'clock Lee had showered and was in bed,
and to all intents and purposes attempting to sleep. It
had been dark for almost twenty minutes, and it
wasn't difficult to pretend she needed the rest. Slowly
she allowed her thoughts to drift, recounting events
from that fateful day two weeks ago when she had first
met Marc. In some ways it seemed almost as if she had
known him from a bygone age, and fate had somehow
taken a hand in forcing recognition.

The sound of tires crunching on gravel brought her
sharply out of her reverie, and she felt every muscle
begin to tense in expectation of Marc's imminent arrival. She gave a hollow laugh that was self-derisory.
Maybe it wasn't Marc at all! But every perceptory
sense told her it was, and she tried to breathe evenly in
an endeavour to still the wild beating of her heart.

Minutes passed—five, or possibly even ten, she had
little idea of the passage of time. At the faint sound of
approaching footsteps she closed her eyes in sudden
panic, then reasoned that it might possibly be Alicia
coming to tell her that Marc had left—except she
hadn't heard the noise of a departing car.

Oh God—if he came into her bedroom, she'd die!
Silently she prayed he would merely knock, and on
receiving no answer would quietly leave.

Lee felt she should have known better, as seconds
later the door opened after a brief peremptory knock,
then the flick of a switch brought an invasion of light.

'Alicia tells me you have a headache,' Marc drawled.
He advanced slowly into the room, dwarfing it significantly, so that all she was aware of was the size of

him and the latent energy he projected.

'Do you doubt it?'

His answer seemed a long time coming, and it took considerable effort for Lee to hold his penetrating gaze. 'Why did you refuse to come to the phone?' he asked in a voice that was deceptively mild.

'I was outside with the children,' she offered stoically, and saw his eyes harden fractionally.

'And the second time?'

'What is this—the third degree?'

For a while he just looked at her, then he threatened softly, 'I would shake you until every bone rattles in your body, do you know that?'

'What's stopping you?' Lee choked bitterly, and he lifted a hand and raked it through his hair in a gesture of impotent rage.

'All right, Lee, I'll allow you benefit of the doubt.' His eyes raked her mercilessly until she felt compelled to look away. 'I came by to issue an invitation to dinner tomorrow evening. Alicia and Stefano have accepted, and Carlo will also be there.'

She remained silent—in fact, she doubted she was capable of uttering so much as a word, and she could have wept when he turned and left the room as abruptly as he had entered it. Minutes later she heard an engine start, followed by the sound of a departing car.

Lee fully expected Alicia to put in an appearance for a résumé of their encounter, and sure enough there was a tentative rap at her door.

'Are you all right?'

Lee endeavoured a carefree smile as her sister entered the room, and failed miserably. 'Yes, of course.'

'He didn't buy it, did he?' Alicia commented with a

wry grimace, and Lee shrugged.

'I didn't really expect him to.'

'Now that he's gone, do you want to get up and watch television? Have some coffee, perhaps?'

'No,' she said wearily. 'Thanks all the same, but I really am tired. I'll have an early night, if you don't mind.'

'Good idea,' Alicia commended with false briskness. 'I'll see you in the morning.' She paused at the open doorway and said slowly, 'I presume Marc told you we're dining at his place tomorrow night?'

Lee acquiesced with a nod of her head, and when the light snapped shut and the door was closed she turned on to her stomach and buried her head beneath the pillow in a gesture of utter hopelessness.

Lee was unable to fault a single aspect of the following evening. Mrs Leone had prepared an elaborate dinner comprising no fewer than four courses, and as a hostess she was utterly captivating, her charm totally uncontrived. Alicia and Stefano were their usual friendly selves, and Carlo provided a welcome relief, ensuring that the conversation never developed a lull, so that after the initial half hour Lee felt some of her inner tension relax. As for Marc, he played the role of an attentive fiancé to perfection, allowing his gaze to linger just that fraction longer than necessary whenever he looked at her—which was often. His smile held a warmth, a depth that appeared genuine, and Lee could only marvel at his acting ability.

It was when Lee was in the kitchen giving Mrs Leone assistance in making coffee almost at the close of the evening that the wedding itself was broached.

'Marc tells me he intends making arrangements for

early in June. Oh, Lee, I'm so pleased it's to be soon,'
that good woman enthused. 'I feel like a young girl
myself just thinking about all the plans we must
make,' she sparkled warmly as she took down cups and
saucers, then she turned and extracted a magnificent
gateau from a nearby cupboard. 'My *pièce de résist-
ance*,' she grinned. 'Terrible for the waistline, but who
cares? Now, before we join the others, I have a suggestion to make. Will you come into town with me on
Monday? We can wander round the shops, sit over
coffee, and talk. Just the two of us,' she added kindly.
'Marc has been like a caged lion these past few days,
and it's been impossible to get anything out of him. In
any case, now the date has definitely been decided
upon, it's really up to you and me to iron out the finer
details. I'll call for you around ten, shall I? In fact, I
think we'll stay on for lunch as well. An hour or two
won't be anywhere near long enough. Now,' she said,
casting the tea-wagon a swift glance, 'shall we take this
into the lounge?'

Lee dreaded the moment they must depart. She
hadn't spent a minute alone with Marc the entire
evening, and she was unsure exactly what he intended
when Carlo rose to his feet and made his farewells.
Alicia and Stefano quickly followed suit, and Lee
moved with them towards the front door, conscious
with spine-tingling awareness of Marc's lazy speculative
gaze.

Expecting any second to hear him declare he would
take her home later, she felt contrarily disappointed
when he walked down the path and held open the rear
door of Stefano's station wagon for her to slip inside.

His, 'Goodnight, darling,' held a tinge of mockery,
and the brief kiss he bestowed on her surprised mouth

was hard and vaguely cruel.

Sunday was an anti-climax, passing as it did with incredible slowness, with Lee on tenterhooks as she
waited for the phone to ring or the familiar sight of
Marc's sleek Fairlane to pull into the gravelled yard.
She showered before dinner and took special care with
her appearance in case he should stop by. When nine
o'clock came and went with still no sign of him, she
gave up and went to bed.

Precisely at ten the next morning Marc's car pulled
into the driveway with Mrs Leone behind the wheel,
and Lee met her at the door with an enthusiasm that
was genuine.

'Good girl, you're ready,' Mrs Leone smiled
warmly. 'I do like punctuality. Oh, we've so much to
do, the time will pass like wildfire. I won't come in,
Alicia,' she refused with a smile. 'Lee and I will get
away.'

It was difficult not to respond to the older woman's
friendliness, and after several minutes of restraint, Lee
cast caution to the wind and entered into the spirit of
the day's enjoyment, permitting herself to be carried
along without thought to the consequences.

Between coffee and lunch they had colours, material
and style decided upon with regard to the bridal
party's apparel. The question of where the reception
should be held was solved without hesitation, for there
was only one hall large enough to accommodate all the
guests Mrs Leone insisted must be issued an
invitation.

'We'll go down to Cairns towards the end of the
week and shop for your trousseau. Then there's your
going away outfit. A suit would be nice—cream linen,

perhaps? It's so fashionable this season, and will be marvellous to wear on the plane.'

Lee controlled her surprise with difficulty, and Mrs Leone pursed her lips in dismay.

'Oh dear. Marc hasn't told you, has he?'

With considerable effort she forced a smile, and ventured lightly, 'Don't keep me in suspense.'

'Hawaii. You're flying out early the morning after the wedding to connect with the flight from Sydney.' Mrs Leone's distress was evident. 'Oh, Lee, forgive me! I didn't mean to spoil the surprise of your honeymoon destination.'

Oh dear, what could she say? 'I promise I'll act surprised,' she managed with an insouciance she was far from feeling, then compounded it by adding, 'I've always wanted to visit there, as I've heard so much about it.'

'You'll love it. Marc and I spent a week there two years ago. It's so different from anywhere else in the world. All that warm sunshine—do you know the temperature varies by only a few degrees all year round?'

It was a further two hours before Mrs Leone considered they had completed all she had set out to do, and by the time Lee arrived back at the farm her head felt as if it didn't belong to her at all.

'Give your sister my love. I'll contact her in a day or two.' Mrs Leone ignited the engine as Lee slipped out from the seat. 'Good heavens, I almost forgot. How careless of me!' she exclaimed with remorse. 'Marc asked me to tell you that he'll call for you at seven. He mentioned something about having a few drinks in town. Goodbye, my dear, I have so enjoyed our day together.' Sketching a cheery wave, she eased the car forward, leaving Lee to gaze after its departing rear with a mixture of amused bewilderment.

As she went indoors she determined that as unpleasant as the prospect might be, she was going to have to insist some sanity be introduced to the whole crazy situation. An argument with Marc wasn't something she looked forward to, for he had proved beyond doubt that he was a formidable opponent.

Consequently Lee dressed with care for the evening ahead, choosing a demure dress in white-spotted black voile with a neckline that came right up to her throat, its slim collar piped with contrasting white. Short sleeves added a tailored effect that was enhanced by a narrow white belt at her waist. Slim-heeled white shoes completed the outfit, and at the sound of a car pulling into the yard she cast a final cursory glance at her mirrored image, then caught up a small clutch-purse and moved out into the lounge.

Marc exuded forceful vitality in casual suede trousers and a dark open-necked shirt, and his indolent appraisal as she entered the room held a touch of mockery that became rapidly more evident as they reached the car.

'Hmm, that perfume packs an evocative punch,' he murmured sardonically as he eased the large vehicle out on to the road and headed it towards town.

'Save it, Marc—I'm not in the mood for subtle sarcasm.'

'My, my,' he mocked lazily. 'That was spoken like a true cynic.'

'I spent the day with your mother,' Lee told him, staring at the rapidly moving countryside beyond the car window. 'Doubtless she related most of the details?'

'Mamma and I share a fine rapport,' he drawled,

and she rounded on him with a vehemence that surprised even herself.

'Marc, we have to talk,' she exploded. 'I simply can't go on like this!'

'I quite agree,' he granted imperturbably, slanting her a glance that held amused tolerance. 'But for an hour or two we'll endeavour not to argue—in fact, we won't mention anything that's likely to cause dissent.'

'They say silence is golden,' Lee quipped with unaccustomed flippancy, and Marc gave a husky chuckle.

'We'll have a drink at the first hotel, then walk uptown to the beer-garden at the Graham,' he suggested, and she merely inclined her head in silent acquiescence.

Somehow Lee managed to maintain an amicable front during the ensuing two hours, although it wasn't easy in view of what was to come. Marc deliberately set out to be an urbane companion, and that he succeeded only served to add fuel to the proverbial fire.

CHAPTER NINE

'MARC, it's going to have to stop,' Lee protested fiercely the instant the car moved out on to the main highway. She felt ready to scream with frustrated anger, and clenched her hands in an effort to control her temper.

'You resemble a volcano about to erupt,' he drawled, sending her a sidelong glance. 'Simmer down, darling,' he advised musingly.

'Don't call me that!' she exclaimed with utter fury,

and gave a gasp of pain as he reached out and caught hold of her hands in a grip that hurt.

'Stop it, Lee,' he commanded brusquely. 'You want to talk—fine. We'll discuss it when we get home. Rationally, over coffee. So control that temper for ten minutes,' he instructed tersely.

'I don't want coffee,' she refused ungraciously. 'I'm not going to allow you to attempt to confuse me.'

His brief glance was openly sardonic. 'Oh, Lee! So I can confuse you?'

You know you can, she thought in stormy silence. All too easily. She couldn't answer him, and she kept her lips tightly closed against the stream of angry words that rose in her throat like bitter gall.

'Out you get.'

'I'm not coming inside,' Lee declared mutinously. Darkness surrounded them, and she gave an involuntary shiver as an awful sense of foreboding crept insidiously over her.

Marc made no attempt to touch her, and she suppressed the thought that he couldn't care less whether she came indoors or not. In any case, what did she have to fear? However unscrupulous Marc was, he would scarcely try to seduce her with his mother in the house.

As if he could read her thoughts, he slid out from the car and made his way towards the house, leaving her little choice other than to follow.

Inside, he tended to the lights and led the way through to the kitchen, and without turning he filled the percolator and set it to simmer. Lee watched with scant patience as he took down two mugs and extracted the sugar bowl, feeling slightly intimidated by his height and breadth in the confines of the room.

'Okay, Lee,' he drawled, swinging round to face her. 'Let's have it.' His eyes were dark, their expression enigmatic, and she had no idea whether his mood was calm or otherwise.

'This—engagement you manipulated,' she rushed quickly. 'Everything is getting out of hand. Your mother is talking about wedding arrangements, and you're doing nothing to dispute it!' Her eyes flared with ill-concealed rage as she glared at him, and her voice rose incredulously. 'You even let everyone assume the marriage is imminent!'

'I fill all your self-professed requirements of a husband,' Marc intoned with deceptive mildness, his gaze disconcertingly level. 'I'm also willing to marry you— so why not comply?'

'Oh, you're being deliberately evasive,' Lee cried, sorely tried. 'I don't want to marry anyone, least of all *you*!'

'Why are you so afraid, Lee?' he taunted softly, and she turned away from him with a gesture of impotent rage.

'I'm going back to Sydney as planned at the end of the week,' she said unsteadily. 'After a decent interval, you can tell everyone we've decided to part. I'm sure you'll think of a suitable reason,' she continued quickly, fixing her gaze on a spot at the far end of the room. 'You won't lack for sympathy,' she added with a trace of bitterness. 'There are at least ten women who'll leap at the chance to take my place.'

For a long time Marc merely looked at her, then he offered slowly, 'Running away won't achieve anything.'

'I'm *not* running away! I came here for a holiday,' she explained angrily as she swung round to face him. 'Hoping to spend most of my time with my sister.

Instead, I've been pressured into accepting innumer-
able invitations I never wanted in the first place.' Her
voice gathered momentum. 'As it is, I've hardly seen
Alicia at all these past two weeks, except for an hour or
two each morning.'

'Then return to Sydney as planned,' he directed
uncompromisingly. 'However, the engagement
stands.'

'*Why?*'

His expression became vaguely cynical. 'You know
the answer to that,' he told her wryly, and she gave a
derisive laugh.

'Lust, Marc? You can alleviate that without much
effort, surely? After all, any woman will do.'

'God in heaven,' he breathed emotively. 'You'd try
the patience of a saint!' Reaching out, he caught hold
of her shoulders in a cruel grip and pulled her towards
him. 'I think it's about time you were taught a lesson,
Lee,' he opined hardily, and before she could do much
else other than utter a startled yelp, she found herself
being hauled unceremoniously across his powerful
thigh about to be on the receiving end of several slaps to
a particularly vulnerable part of her anatomy.

The instant Lee was free she flew at him in a rage,
arms flailing wildly as she struck out with her fists,
aiming for any part of that muscular frame she could
make contact with. 'How dare you! Oh!' Words temporarily failed her. 'I hate you!'

Strong hands caught hers and held them with
effortless ease, bringing her wildly struggling body to
a halt. 'In that case, I have nothing to lose,' Marc
averred harshly as he pulled her close, then his mouth
was on hers, punishing in a way that made her want to
die.

It went on and on, until Lee thought she must

surely slip into the black void which threatened to engulf her. He held her so tightly she felt her ribs might crack, and after a while she lay quiescent in his arms, too emotionally and physically drained to attempt an escape.

When at last he released her she stood silent, her vision becoming blurred with the tears that welled and trickled slowly down her cheeks. Unable to bear him witness her humiliation, she turned away, and would have run if her legs could have supported her. Head bent, she reached blindly for a nearby chair, then to her utter horror she felt her body sway of its own accord and she gave a frightened cry.

The next instant she was airborne, held firmly against a rock-hard chest, and Marc's husky string of oaths made her blanch as he carried her from the room.

Lee felt too weary to bother taking note of where they were heading, and she was dimly aware of cream-papered walls and a hallway, then the quiet snapping sound of a door closing brought her head upwards as she shakily brushed back a curtain of hair from off her face.

'Marc, put me down!' Her voice gained strength as she glimpsed the room's furnishings, and it rose in panic when her eyes caught sight of the large double bed. 'Whose room is this?'

'Mine,' he informed her dryly, and moving towards the bed he pulled back the coverlet and laid her down. 'Stay there. I'll be back with some coffee.' His tone brooked no argument, and Lee didn't have the strength to disobey him.

When he returned seconds later she struggled to sit upright, and took the mug he extended with both hands. The sweet hot milky brew brought some colour to her cheeks, reviving her as she slowly sipped the contents. Her mouth felt stiff and faintly bruised—and her pride stung when she thought of the humiliation he'd almost inflicted on her. Enervated to a point beyond even tears, she was sure if he touched her the cracks threading her delicate eggshell-like façade would splinter and expose her vulnerable heart. Shakily she held out the empty mug and moved to swing her legs towards the floor.

'Thank you, I'm all right now.' She stood to her feet and instantly regretted the action, for it brought her close to Marc—much too close. 'Will you please take me home?'

Very gently he lifted a hand and pushed back a lock of hair behind her ear, then his fingers trailed down to her chin, tilting it slightly so she had little option but to look at him. Slowly he lifted his other hand and cupped her face, and his expression was impossible to fathom as he let his gaze wander over her finely-boned features.

Her lips moved of their own volition, but no sound emerged, and she moistened them with the edge of her tongue. His eyes flared momentarily, then darkened with an emotion she was afraid to define. 'Marc— please!' Was that her voice? It sounded like the whisper of a disembodied being and totally unrelated to herself.

'Don't say anything,' he said quietly as he brushed his lips across her forehead. Softly he feathered a butterfly kiss to each eyelid in turn, then trailed down to the edge of her mouth.

Lee felt her lips tremble, and a slow pulsing ache began deep in her stomach as he teased them lightly with tantalising evocativeness so that unconsciously she strained towards him, parting her mouth and inviting his possession.

The taste of his kiss brought a response she was unable to hide, and her arms crept slowly up to wind around his neck. The feel of his hands on her body set each nerve-end tingling alive until her whole being felt like a tightly-tuned string. She was aware of a hunger in him that was no less than her own, and she wanted more than this partial slaking of their emotions.

There was no thought to deny him when his hands moved to release the long zip fastening at the back of her dress, and she gave a small sigh when the clip on her bra freed the fullness of her breasts. As his lips travelled down from the hollow of her throat to the rising swell below she began to quiver, and when he took a rosy peak into his mouth she experienced a shaft of such incredible pleasure that it was all she could do not to cry out.

Scarcely being aware of doing so she let her fingers move to undo the buttons on his shirt, and when it had been discarded she began creating subtle patterns with her fingertips on the mat of hair covering his chest, arousing forth a husky growl from the depths of his throat.

Their slow appraisal of each other's bodies assumed an intimacy from which there could be no drawing back, and as if in a dream Lee became aware they were no longer standing. A heady floating sensation seemed to render her limbs to jelly as he carried her to the bed, and her eyes widened as she caught a glimpse of the naked emotion evident in the instant before he covered her mouth with his own.

Lee was lost beneath the mastery of his touch, as

with undoubted expertise he sought to bring alive each sensual pleasure centre. With his mouth and his hands he created havoc in parts of her body no man had previously been permitted to explore.

Vaguely she became aware of an increasing urgency in his leashed strength, then his legs were between her own and there was no mistaking his intention.

Dear God—*no*! In blind panic she began to struggle, his name on her lips. 'Marc——'

Her cry was stilled by his mouth, and her silent scream sounded no more than a tortured moan in her throat. It wasn't her imagination that she felt his body stiffen.

'Dear Mother of God,' Marc breathed in a barely audible groan. 'Why didn't you tell me?'

Lee moved her head from side to side in an effort to escape the tearing pain, and as it began to subside she gave a whimper of protest as she felt his powerful body move. 'Don't!' The single plea emerged as a begging whisper.

'Trust me, darling.'

With a gentleness that brought a sob to her lips he set about using all the expertise at his command to re-awaken her desire, and at last their spirits rose in one accord to a tumultuous crescendo, the like of which she had never dreamed possible.

Lee supposed she must have slept, although it couldn't have been for long, and she came drowsily awake to the touch of lips playing a provocative tune along the sensitive cord of her neck. She felt deliciously lethargic, yet alive in a way that brought a dreamy sparkle to her eyes as she turned her head slightly.

'What am I doing here?' she smiled, genuinely bemused, and Marc's mouth twitched with humour.

'You mean you don't know?' he queried teasingly,
and as his eyes flared with renewed passion she hastily
hid her heated cheeks into the curve of his neck.

This time his lovemaking was slow and languorous,
and the ecstasy he aroused reached an inevitable
conclusion that was no less satisfying than before.

Endless minutes later, Marc slid off the bed and
scooped her into his arms.

'Where are you taking me?' Lee queried breathlessly
as he moved out into the hallway. 'Marc?' An un-
bidden thought occurred. 'Have you no shame?' she
whispered tremulously. 'What if your mother——'

'Mamma elected to stay with friends overnight,' he
slanted quizzically.

'Oh.'

His mouth curved to form a musing smile. 'Just—
"oh", Lee?'

For the moment she could think of nothing to say,
and his husky laughter brought a faint blush to her
cheeks.

Opening a door on his left, Marc stepped into the
room and flicked a trio of switches that bathed everything in a subdued glow from several muted strategi-
cally-placed lamps. Lee glanced around with a feeling
of awe, noting the beautifully-styled spa-pool set on a
slightly raised dais, the lush green deep-piled carpet,
and the eye-catching walls with their alternate panel-
ling of mirrors and silk-embossed neptunian-designed
tapestries.

The gentle surging water from the pool provided
the only sound, and Lee couldn't help the appreciative
murmur that escaped her lips as Marc lowered her
down into the silken warmth.

'Like it?'

She turned her face towards him with an enchanting smile. 'Who could help but like it? It's incredible.'

'Another first, Lee?' Marc demanded gently, and she felt suddenly shy of this large man who could both torment and delight with amazing ease.

The past few hours had seemed like a dream, a fantasy in which she had been an ethereal participant, and she never wanted it to end.

'What's going on in that funny little head of yours?' he demanded, and moving close he cupped her face and bestowed a lingering kiss. 'Does it embarrass you to be here with me like this?' His mouth moved back and forth on hers, gently at first, then with an increasing ardour, awakening a matching hunger that seemed to spring from the very depths of her soul. 'I never want to be apart from you,' he said huskily. 'We belong together. Kiss me,' he commanded softly, and when she touched her lips against his in a butterfly caress he gave a throaty chuckle and held her away. 'My darling Lee,' he chastised devilishly, 'I shall have to teach you to do better than that.'

Lee felt her eyes widen as he moved to the pool's side, and her lids veiled her confusion as he levered himself out.

'You can look now, little Miss Prim,' he teased laughingly as he hitched a towel about his hips.

Colour seemed to suffuse her entire body, and she proffered defensively, 'Perhaps you wouldn't mind turning your back? I'd like to get out.'

Marc's eyes gleamed with hidden laughter as he tossed her a towel, then he obediently turned away and within seconds Lee was out of the pool and had enveloped herself in the huge fluffy towel.

'It's a little late for modesty,' his voice drawled

lazily, and she glanced up and saw his eyes twinkling
wickedly in the mirrored reflection before he turned to
face her. 'Come back to bed,' he bade gently, although
there was nothing gentle about the way he was regarding her, and a wave of incredible shyness swept over
her so that she had difficulty in finding her voice.

'Please,' she managed at last. 'It's awfully late. I
must go home.'

Marc gazed at her unwaveringly for what seemed an
age, then he moved with catlike fluidity, his stance
relaxed and totally at ease as he crossed to her side.

Lee was aware of his latent masculinity to a point
where she found it almost impossible to breathe nor-
mally, and every nerve in her body tingled vibrantly
alive as he curved an arm round her waist and hugged
her close to his side.

'We have to talk,' he declared, moving with her towards the door. 'Although I must admit it's the last
thing on my mind at the moment.' His wry smile went
unnoticed as he brushed his lips over her hair.

When they reached the bedroom Marc drew her
over to the large bed, and Lee felt her body begin to
tremble as they sank down on to it. Gently he moved
her hair aside, then his lips sought her vulnerable
nape, seducing in a way that made her discard all her
inhibitions as she turned into his arms.

Cradled closely beside him, Lee stared into the
shadowed darkness. Marc's even breathing indicated
that he was asleep, and she was afraid to move lest she
disturbed him. Soon, she decided silently. The
minutes ticked slowly by, and with each came an increasing sense of turmoil as her mind registered the
implications of her own folly.

Dear God, it didn't bear thinking about. A silent

groan escaped her lips. How could she have been so
blind as to have let Marc seduce her—and without so
much as a token resistance? Remembering the intimacies she had permitted brought shame, and an abject
humiliation. A master of sensual expertise, Marc had
utilised all the skill at his command to bring about her
seduction.

One thing for sure—she couldn't stay here! The
thought of facing his possible rejection was sufficient
to galvanise her into action.

Hardly daring to breathe, Lee eased the sleep-heavy
arm that pinned her body close to his, then gradually
she began to inch carefully away towards the side of
the bed. Any minute she expected Marc to stir, and as
she slipped her feet to the floor she felt her heart
pound, and sound seeming so loud that she was sure
he must hear it.

With stealthy cautious steps she located her clothes,
donning them with deliberate slowness, resisting the
temptation to fling them on and flee the house and the
compelling man who owned it.

There was one bad moment when Lee emerged outside and encountered Bruno keeping guard at the
bottom of the steps. For a heartstopping second she
thought he was going to bark, but quick thinking
saved the day, and she murmured his name in a quiet
authoritative voice and bade him stay.

It was slightly more than half a mile to Alicia and
Stefano's farm, yet her breathing when she reached
their driveway was as ragged as if she had run all the
way.

Relief at having escaped from Marc brought a release of tension, and with it came reaction. A shaking
mass of nerves, Lee barely made it to her room before

she collapsed in a heap on her bed. She was too numb to cry, and she sat for an undetermined length of time staring blankly at the opposite wall.

The first pale streaks of dawn, accompanied by the rooster's crow jarred her subconscious, and displaying an icy calm Lee stood to her feet and systematically set about packing. Then she gathered a fresh change of clothes and made for the bathroom, completing her shower and attending to her toilette with concentrated dedication.

'Lee, you're an early bird this morning. I expected you to sleep late.'

Lee turned from her passage down the hall and met Alicia's warm smile. Shaking her head, she said quietly, 'Are the children awake?'

'No, praise be. Although I'm expecting an ear-splitting yell any minute. Shall I make some coffee? We might manage five minutes of peace, if we're lucky.'

Resolve lent her strength. 'I have to leave, Alicia,' she began without preamble. 'And it has to be today.'

Her sister's face ran a gamut of emotions. 'There's nothing I can do to dissuade you?' she queried carefully, and Lee shook her head.

'Am I permitted to ask why?'

Lee lifted a hand and ran shaky fingers through the length of her hair. 'I'd rather you didn't.'

'Just one question—does Marc know you're going?'

Lee turned away and began walking towards her room. 'I've packed everything, as you can see.' She waved an encompassing hand, then let it fall to her side as she crossed to the dressing-table.

'It's that bad?' Alicia demanded gently, her eyes clouding with concern as she saw her sister make the studiously careful movements of an automaton.

'Worse.'

'Give me your ticket reservation,' Alicia instructed quietly. 'I'll ring through to Cairns and change it to today's midday flight.' Their eyes met in the mirror, and the sisterly bond had no need of words. 'As far as Stefano is concerned, we're off to Cairns for a day's shopping. We'll simply drop the children off at his parents' house on the way through town.'

CHAPTER TEN

IT was all so simple that afterwards Lee could only wonder at the ease with which she managed to escape.

During breakfast the children provided a welcome distraction, although she was scarcely conscious of their demands as most of it passed right over her head. Only when the phone rang just prior to their departure did Lee experience a few hellish seconds, and her eyes riveted on the receiver as Alicia answered, her expression assuming that of a cornered animal until a silent negative shake dismissed the caller as being Marc.

Safetly past the Mareeba township and on to the highway leading towards Kuranda, Lee began to relax somewhat. Alicia, bless her heart, chattered about inconsequential things that had little bearing on anything, so all that was required of Lee was the uttering of a monosyllabic comment here and there.

The large station wagon pulled into the car park adjacent to the Ansett air terminal in Cairns with less than ten minutes to spare until check-in time, and while Alicia locked up Lee extracted her luggage from the trunk and carried it the short distance to the office.

Several people milled around the entrance, and inside the queue of fellow passengers waiting at the baggage check-in necessitated a moderate delay before Lee was able to rejoin her sister.

'I left my ring in the top left-hand drawer of the dressing-table,' Lee said matter-of-factly. 'I'd appreciate it if you would give it to Marc whenever you happen to see him next.' At Alicia's nod, she walked towards a nearby desk and joined the queue awaiting seat allocations.

'Shall I get you a magazine to read on the plane?'

Lee shook her head. 'I'll write within the next few days,' she said, deadly calm, and she even managed to summon something resembling a smile, although from the look on Alicia's face the attempt wasn't entirely successful.

'Ring me instead. Reverse the charges,' her sister insisted anxiously.

'The whole thing was a charade from start to finish,' Lee told her stoically. The hand holding her ticket was surprisingly steady. Outwardly she was calm, and apparently unaffected by the wrenching turmoil gnawing at her insides. 'I'm an utter mess,' she mocked silently, 'and not a soul could tell.' Oh God, if only she could dissolve into tears! She daren't permit herself the weakness, otherwise her shrewdly astute sister might guess the truth.

'Is there any message you'd like me to give Marc?' Alicia ventured carefully, and Lee shook her head.

'You're very dear to me, but please don't interfere.'

The announcement of her flight came over the tannoy, and minutes later she was giving Alicia a hug prior to walking out on to the tarmac to board the plane.

The flight south was uneventful, and Lee didn't utter so much as a word except for a monosyllabic acceptance or refusal of the hostess's ministrations. During the stopover in Brisbane she remained on board, unaware of anything or anyone on the plane, and upon touchdown in Sydney she collected her luggage and summoned a taxi with the motions of a robot.

Only Sam was home, and she treated his stunned surprise with a forced grin. 'If you care for me at all, just get me a drink—a stiff one.' She dropped her suitcase, thrust down the overnight bag, and sank into a chair.

'One gin and tonic coming up,' Sam declared with droll cynicism, moving to the cabinet and unscrewing a selection of bottles. 'Here,' he advised, handing her the glass. 'Do I melt out of sight and leave you to your misery, or do I join you?'

'If you disappear, I'll kill you!' Lee began with a fierceness that brought Sam's eyebrows soaring towards his hairline.

'That bad?'

'I should never have gone on holiday.'

'I'm amazed,' Sam drawled lazily. 'I thought you were immune.'

Lee glanced at him without comprehension, and he smiled.

'From the opposite sex, sweetheart,' he explained, and she scowled.

'Don't be ridiculous!'

'He must be quite something if you turned tail and scuttled home.'

'I did not *scuttle*—I merely chose to return earlier than intended,' she insisted with marked aloofness, and he laughed.

'Honey, this is Sam, remember?' he mocked gently.

'Big brother Sam,' she said with some asperity. 'A girl's best friend—adviser, advocate and protector.'

'That's all you'd ever let me be,' he answered wryly, lifting a glass to his lips and draining half the contents in one long swallow. 'Do we quietly drink ourselves into oblivion, or do you want to talk?'

'Let's go out,' Lee begged, a slight edge of desperation in her voice. 'All four of us. Somewhere bright and noisy. Please,' she added, and missed the gleam of anger that flashed momentarily in Sam's eyes.

'Why not?' He watched her diminish her drink with total disregard for its effects. 'Ease up, Lee,' he advised bluntly. 'That stuff is pretty potent.'

'I don't need a lecture, Sam.'

'Damn him to hell!' The words came out in an angry rush, and her eyes widened fractionally, swift comprehension and sadness twisting her lips into a better smile.

'He's invincible—the original dark angel.' Laughter choked in her throat. 'The flames of hell wouldn't touch him!'

The front door banged, accompanied by a light banter of male and female voices, and by the time Carl and Trudi burst into the lounge Sam's face was an enigmatic mask.

'By all that's holy, what are you doing home?'

'Lee, what happened? Is something wrong?' Trudi demanded, her pert features assuming concern as she scrutinised her friend.

'We're eating out—on me,' Sam intimated, collecting Lee's empty glass and his own. 'Get changed into something suitable—we're going to sound out a few of the city's discos.'

'That's an offer I won't refuse,' Trudi decided with a twinkle of amusement. 'Carl?'

'Oh, definitely,' the tall lanky young man responded unhesitatingly, and Lee felt moved to tears.

Like the true friends they were, they rallied without reservation. 'Half an hour?' she queried lightly. 'I need a shower after being in a plane for nearly five hours.'

'Not a minute longer,' Sam announced with mock severity. 'Otherwise I'll withdraw my offer.'

'Where are we going to eat?' Trudi demanded. 'How about Angelo's? I love Italian food.'

Sam glimpsed the fleeting spasm of pain flicker momentarily across Lee's expressive features. 'Chinese,' he said firmly. 'I'm paying, remember?'

On the surface Lee was a sparkling companion, laughing, and later when they danced, she was one of the most energetic on the floor. Only the very discerning would have guessed the effort it cost her to maintain an air of such cheerfulness, but it had the desired effect in promoting exhaustion so that she slept soundlessly until seven the following morning.

'You're not going in to work?' Trudi exclaimed with disbelief as Lee set about making herself breakfast.

'Why not?' Lee parried. 'What else can I do?'

'But you're not expected back until Monday!' the other girl wailed. 'Besides, you look ghastly.'

'Thanks! That's just what I need to improve my morale.'

'Oh, you know what I mean,' Trudi said quickly, and Lee lifted an expressive eyebrow.

'Do I?'

'Want to talk about it?' Trudi offered tentatively, but Lee shook her head.

'Not yet.' She summoned a slight smile, unaware of the haunted expression in her eyes that made her appear strangely vulnerable. 'I'd better hurry if I'm to make the eight o'clock train.' Food was abhorrent, and she sipped the strong black coffee, then discarded half the contents down the sink.

In her room she quickly dressed, applied a minimum of make-up, then slipped her feet into backless sandals before grabbing her shoulder-bag. A sketchy wave as she passed the kitchen was meant to encompass the trio sitting around the table, then she opened the front door and emerged out into the cool morning air.

Apart from expressing initial surprise at Lee's return, her co-workers accepted her presence with gratitude, for the city salon was heavily booked and an extra pair of hands made the work-load considerably lighter.

The day passed quickly, and the next, with Lee pouring all her energy into work, and in the evening she retired to her room soon after dinner pleading the necessity for an early night. She was aware that her friends were anxious about her well-being, but she hurt too much inside to reveal any confidences. All she wanted to do was to crawl into some protective shell and hide until her raw emotions began to heal.

There were times during the following days when she thought she might be going out of her mind, for Marc's forceful image crowded all her waking moments, and even sleep brought little respite. More than once she woke from turbulent dreams that assumed nightmarish proportions, so that she tossed and turned until morning and rose feeling totally enervated.

Lee had imagined that with time it would get better, but it only became worse as each day progressed. Three weeks, and still she resembled a walking zombie! She had lost weight, valuable pounds that reduced her sylph-like figure to positive thinness, and sleep was something she was only able to covet for a few scant hours each night. Work had proved no panacea for grief, nor had throwing herself into an exhaustive social whirl.

Sam, Carl, and Trudi saw to it that she was rarely alone, and already mention of a party had been casually tossed in her direction as she had entered the spacious old house in suburban Moroubra less than ten minutes previously. In spite of having spent an exhausting day at work she supposed she would go—anything was better than spending an evening in lonely isolation.

'Lee!' Sam's voice called from behind the closed door. 'Can you come out? There's someone here to see you.'

Who on earth could be calling at this time of day? Lee puzzled with a frown. Slipping her feet to the floor, she threw down the letter she had begun to Alicia, straightened her skirt, ran her fingers quickly through the length of her hair, then emerged out into the hall.

The only other occupant in the lounge besides Sam was a tall dark-haired man whose broad frame was achingly familiar, and Lee came to a sudden halt a few steps inside the room.

'Hello, Lee.'

For a heartstopping moment she thought her voice had become frozen in her throat, then the constriction seemed to lessen, and she gave a slight nod. 'Marc,' she acknowledged with icy politeness, then seeing his faintly raised eyebrow, she effected the necessary introductions. 'Sam Hetherington—Marc Leone.'

Marc's eyes never left hers, although their expression was inscrutable. His casual attire reflected an elegance due to superb tailoring, and her pulse began to race crazily just at the sight of him.

'Do you want me to stay?'

Lee glanced abstractedly towards Sam, and for a moment she remained undecided. 'No—thanks,' she refused slowly, and with a curt nod Sam walked to the door, then he halted and turned towards Marc.

'If you hurt her again, I'll kill you!'

Lee spared him an anguished glance, then the door clicked shut and she was alone with the one man she thought never to set eyes on again.

'What are you doing here?' she demanded in a voice that was faintly breathless, and the fact that his presence had such a devastating effect on her made her incredibly angry.

Marc stood regarding her silently for what seemed an age, then he drawled silkily, 'You have a very—loyal friend.'

She flushed slightly at his tone, and hidden sparks turned her eyes to molten gold. 'Sam regards me as a sister.'

One eyebrow ascended in a cynical gesture. 'His affection goes beyond brotherly love.'

'Your perception amazes me,' Lee threw disparagingly, and Marc inclined his head with undisguised mockery. With concentrated effort she held his gaze, and demanded, 'Is this a social call? I'm rather busy.'

He looked at her in silence, his regard deep and incredibly solemn before declaring softly, 'You know why I'm here.'

'Do I? Forgive me, but I don't possess mental telepathy.'

Marc's eyes narrowed fractionally. 'Did you imagine I'd let you disappear?'

She gave a slight shrug. 'Why not?' She shifted her attention to a spot some distance away, then returned it to the third button on his dark brown shirt.

'You know damned well why not!'

Lee felt warm colour tinge her cheeks, and it took all her resolve to force coolness into her voice. 'Conscience, Marc?' she slanted with apparent unconcern, and was immediately aware of his anger.

'Lee,' he began dangerously, and she broke in furiously,

'Oh, for heaven's sake! I'm not a naïve young teenager. What—happened wasn't such an earth-shattering experience.' Liar, she discounted mentally, then she met his gaze with renewed determination. 'I guess I should be grateful to you for destroying a myth, and releasing my inhibitions.'

Marc's husky oath sent a chill tingling down the length of her spine. 'Dammit, Lee, have you any idea how I felt when I discovered you'd gone?'

'Oh, should I have waited until morning?' she parried with saccharine sweetness. 'Forgive me—I'm unversed in the ethics regarding such matters.'

His eyes were frighteningly bleak. 'My God, I could shake you until your teeth rattle!' He thrust his hands into his trouser pockets, and Lee suppressed a shiver. 'I was equally responsible for what happened between us—more so, perhaps, than you.'

Catching her hands together behind her back, she met his eyes unflinchingly. 'Don't worry—I'm not pregnant.'

'Is that why you think I'm here?' he demanded savagely. 'To check on the outcome?' Without seeming to move, he was suddenly within touching distance.

'Isn't it?'

For a moment she thought he was going to strike her, and she took an involuntary step backwards at the same time as his hands descended with biting strength to grasp each shoulder.

'Marc,' she protested painfully, 'you're hurting me!'

'Not half as much as I'd like to!' With an angry movement he thrust her away from him, then he lifted a hand to his hair, raking it emotively into unruly disarray. 'The only time you're not spitting at me like an angry kitten is when I have you in my arms,' he drawled with wry cynicism.

'Where I'll never be again,' Lee insisted quickly, and saw his lips twist into a mocking smile.

'No? Somehow I think it's inevitable.'

'Never!' She was so incensed she stamped her foot. 'I'm no man's possession—much less yours. Dear God, you're so impossible, no sane woman could bear with you!'

'Think of the making up we'll do after our many fights,' Marc drawled, and Lee gasped in outrage.

'We hate each other,' she threw vehemently, and he gave a soundless laugh.

'Not all the time, Lee.'

'What does that prove?' she demanded.

'You belong to me.' The very quietness of his voice made her shiver, and she shook her head slowly.

'No.' The denial come from her lips as an anguished whisper. 'Go away, Marc,' she begged. 'Our relationship has been disastrous from start to finish. I just want to forget it ever happened.'

For a long while he simply stood still, his eyes dark with an emotion she was unable to fathom, then at last he said quietly, 'Do you think you can?'

Unable to face him, she turned away and gazed out the window at the fading light. Within a few minutes it would be dark. If only Marc would go, she thought with something verging close to desperation. Much longer, and she'd break down, and she had no wish for him to witness her tears.

Scant seconds later she sensed him move to stand behind her, and every last nerve-end began to quiver as she felt him brush aside her hair, then his lips touched her vulnerable nape in a feathery caress, and she held her breath as he traced the gentle curve of her neck. A silent moan escaped her as he turned her round to face him.

'Don't Marc,' Lee begged. 'Please.'

'Don't—what?' he taunted softly. 'Kiss you?' He gave a harsh laugh, and his eyes darkened measurably. 'I might as well try not to breathe.' His head lowered and his lips brushed hers, tantalising, evocative, and she felt the familiar aching need course through her limbs, rendering them weak and totally malleable.

Of their own volition her hands crept up over his shoulders to clasp together behind his neck, and when his mouth fastened hungrily on hers there was no thought to deny him.

It was only timeless minutes later that common sense returned, and with it a certain amount of anger, so that she broke the embrace and attempted to step away from him.

'This isn't going to solve anything, Marc,' she began with determination, and saw the faint gleam of amusement in his eyes as he regarded her.

'I'd say it's a step in the right direction.'

'What direction is that?' she demanded, her hazel eyes steady, and his mouth twisted into a wry smile.

'Why did you run away, Lee?' he parried quietly.

'You achieved your objective,' she reiterated defensively. 'Let's just say I didn't plan on staying around for a repeat performance.'

'Is that what you thought I had in mind?' His demand was silky-smooth and dangerous.

'Oh, you're pretty persuasive, Marc,' she said bitterly. 'And experienced,' she added with a harsh laugh. 'My God, I didn't really stand a chance, did I? Like a peach, ripe for the picking!'

'Stop it!' Marc commanded brusquely, giving her an ungentle shake, and she struggled to get free, becoming enraged at her impotent efforts as he effortlessly stilled her flailing arms.

'I hate you!' Lee spat in a fine temper. 'Do you understand—I *hate* you!'

Marc's hands tightened with painful intensity over her slim shoulders. 'You really are the most stubborn, wilful, *blind* young woman it's ever been my misfortune to meet,' he growled emotively. 'I'm torn between slapping your delightful rear, and kissing you senseless.'

Lee's eyes sparked with ill-concealed fury. 'If you lay one finger on me, I'll never forgive you!'

His silence was enervating, then without warning he hauled her close and his mouth crushed hers in a pitiless assault that became mercilessly brutal as he ravaged her soft lips, leaving her gasping and soundlessly moaning for breath.

At last it came to an end, and he flung her away in disgust. 'You bring out the beast in me,' he thrust bluntly and without apology. One hand lifted and he ran a hand roughly through his hair. 'Heaven help me!' His husky oath was self-derisory. 'I came down here clear in my mind what I wanted to say. Yet within ten minutes we're engaged in a full-scale verbal war, and I've resorted to threating you with nothing less than brutality.'

'It's hopeless,' Lee muttered through painfully bruised lips, and her stomach lurched as his hands caught hold of her waist.

'What *is* hopeless is our being apart,' Marc declared bluntly, his eyes dark with ill-concealed passion, and Lee offered shakily,

'Yet together we fight like demented animals.'

'Only because we're both too damned proud to admit we love each other.'

Lee stood absolutely still, her heart almost seeming to stop for an instant before beginning to pound with a thundering beat. 'Are you trying to say——'

'I love you,' Marc finished softly. 'Quite shockingly, in fact,' he acknowledged a trifle wryly. 'If you'd waited, I would have told you.' His eyes gleamed, the love light unmistakable in their depths. 'I fell asleep with the vision of kissing you awake and imparting that fact. Instead, you stole off in the early hours of the morning.' His mouth tightened a fraction, and his hands clenched painfully about her waist. 'When I rang the farm it was to discover from Stefano that you and Alicia had departed an hour previously for a day's shopping in Cairns. It wasn't until evening that I was acquainted with the fact that you were by then in Sydney.' At her gasp of pain he gave a husky exclamation and drew her close. 'Perhaps it was as well there were a few thousand miles separating us,' he mused dryly, 'otherwise I think I would have killed you.'

Lee tentatively slid her arms around his waist, and allowed herself the giddy pleasure of resting her head against that broad expanse of chest. 'Why didn't you phone, or write me?' she asked, her voice muffled, and some of the hurt she'd suffered was evident.

'Do you imagine I didn't want to?' Marc groaned, enfolding her close against him. 'Oh God, Lee, it was all I could do not to get the next plane after you.' His lips brushed the top of her head, and his urgent need of her became achingly obvious. 'The one thing that stopped me was the knowledge that you needed breathing space. My pursuit of you had been intense,' he elaborated with a trace of mockery. 'I swept you

way out of your depth, mindless of your fears or
doubts. If I'd come after you too soon, you'd have
only imagined I was browbeating you into submission.' He pushed her gently away from him and tilted
her chin. 'I knew my mind, and I was almost certain I
knew yours,' he smiled gently. 'All you needed was
time—time alone in which to think.'

Lee digested his words in silence, and unable to restrain the need to hurt him a little, she murmured,
'What if you're wrong?'

For an instant there was naked pain in those dark
depths, and she shook her head in anguish, at once
contrite. 'Oh Marc, no,' she said brokenly, and clasp-
ing her arms around that hard muscular frame she
hugged him close. 'I love you—I think I always have.
These past few weeks have been hell,' she enlightened
in an aching voice. 'I thought I'd never see you again,
and I wanted to die.'

Marc grasped her chin firmly and lifted it to meet
his gaze. 'Little vixen,' he berated roughly. 'For a
moment I almost——'

Lee placed a hand over his mouth, silencing him.
'Forgive me,' she begged, her eyes filling with tears.
'Knowing you hasn't been easy,' she began by way of
explanation. 'You never once indicated how you really
felt—not even after trapping me into an engagement. I
thought you were just playing with me, amusing yourself at my expense,' she ended miserably.

His kiss was long and entirely satisfactory, leaving
her bemused and breathless.

'I was lost almost from the first time I set eyes on you,'
Marc mused with a smile. 'There you were—late, flustered, and startlingly beautiful.' His slight chuckle was
disarming. 'I held my breath all the way to Townsville,' he revealed, pausing to bestow a brief hard kiss on

her parted mouth. 'It seemed too good to be true when you travelled on to Cairns and were met by Alicia. Even then I determined I would have you—with typical male egotistical conceit,' he added wryly. 'I'd amassed sufficient experience to be sure I could break down your resistance. However, you defied me at every turn—infuriating me to a point whereby I was hardly responsible for my actions. No matter how often I resolved to treat you gently, you inevitably moved me to a savagery I had never imagined myself capable of. Never before have I wanted to kiss a woman and beat her—both at the same time!'

'You did,' Lee reminded him drolly. 'Frequently.'

Marc's subdued laughter brought an answering smile. 'With two such combustible parents, I rather fear for our children,' he declared with dry cynicism, and she felt her cheeks tinge a telling pink. 'When are you going to marry me?' he demanded gently.

'I wasn't aware that I'd been asked.'

'You doubt my intentions?'

Lee placed a placating hand on his arm. 'The first time didn't count, Marc.'

'Minx!' he chided with a lazy grin. 'Do you want me down on bended knee?'

'No.' A laugh gurgled in her throat. 'That would be asking too much.'

'Lee Carruthers, will you do me the honour of becoming my wife?' he demanded with undue solemnity, and her heart seemed to take wings and soar heavenward.

'Oh yes, please!'

'Saturday?'

Her face paled slightly. 'So soon?'

'Why not? I have the licence, an appointment with the priest at four o'clock on Saturday afternoon. My mother has a guest list for the wedding, and just as soon as I phone her, she'll begin contacting them.'

Consternation widened her eyes. 'A church wedding? Marc, I haven't a suitable dress. There's a hundred things to do, and I haven't even done one of them!' she wailed.

'Nonsense. We'll have time to shop for something suitable before catching the plane tomorrow.'

'Marc——'

'Shh, darling. Don't make obstacles where there are none,' he remonstrated softly. 'Go and change while I ring your sister. We're going out for the evening to celebrate—candlelit dinner, champagne. Somewhere quiet and intimate.'

'And afterwards?'

Marc leant down and kissed her with bruising intensity. 'Afterwards, my sweet, I deliver you home, and go on to my apartment. The next time I have you in my bed I want it to be with you as my wife.'

A soft smile lit her features, and her eyes sparkled with devilish humour. 'Such restraint—how noble, Marc!'

'You'll pay for that remark,' he growled, pushing her firmly from him, and she laughed, delighting in teasing him.

'Is that a threat or a promise?'

'Both,' he declared succinctly. 'Now, go before I change my mind and exact due penance.'

On reflection, Lee had little recollection of the forty-eight hours preceding her marriage to Marc, for the details were a hazy glow. Even the ceremony itself held a dreamlike quality, and the reception afterwards passed in a blur of faces, food she hardly tasted and a quantity of superb wine.

It was after ten before they were able to tear themselves away from family and friends and begin the drive down the Range to Cairns, from where they would fly out to Hawaii the following morning for a glorious two weeks.

'You don't need to,' Lee told him solemnly a matter of minutes after entering their motel unit close to the Esplanade in Cairns.

'I don't need to—what?' Marc drawled teasingly as he came to stand behind her. 'Are you implying I shouldn't make love to you?' His arms curved round her slim form and he drew her back against him, his hands lightly caressing her breasts, and she turned to face him.

'Go so far away, or have a honeymoon at all,' she said softly, her eyes very bright at the glimpse of slumbering passion in those dark eyes regarding her so intently.

'Practising being a thrifty wife so soon?' he questioned lightly, moulding her close so that she was aware of every muscular curve. 'I can well afford it, my sweet.'

'It's not that,' she said in a muffled voice, and he frowned slightly.

'Then what is it? Don't you like Hawaii? We'll go somewhere else.'

'That's just it,' Lee burst out. 'We don't need to go *anywhere*. Marc, I'd be just as happy to stay here in Cairns, or over at Green Island. Don't you see?' she implored. 'As long as we're together, it doesn't matter where.'

His mouth twisted into a gentle smile, then it wasn't gentle at all as it fastened on hers in a kiss that transported her to a dreamlike realm of sensual awareness, so that she felt strangely bereft when at last he lifted his head.

'I'm inclined to agree with you,' he mused a trifle

wryly. 'However, the first few weeks after marriage are rather special, and besides,' he grinned tolerantly, 'I rather fancy showing you the sights of that magnificent group of islands—in between other things.'

Lee's eyes gleamed mischievously alive as she tilted her chin. 'Such as?'

'Making love to you—often,' Marc declared emotively, and she laughed a little, delighting in provoking him.

'Then you'd better make a start, hadn't you?'

'Is that an invitation?'

'Do you need one?'

For an instant there was a momentary glimpse of something like regret in his dark eyes, and with perceptive understanding she placed a finger across his lips.

'Don't, Marc,' she begged. 'The past, with all its misunderstanding and hurt, is gone. "Tomorrow is the first day of the rest of our lives". That's very true, don't you think?'

He lifted his hands and gently cupped her face, and his voice became husky with emotion as he spoke. 'You're beautiful, do you know that? An inner beauty that has no connection with the shape and look of you.' He lowered his head and softly placed his mouth against hers in a fleeting sensual caress. 'Dear God in heaven, I love you,' he groaned huskily.

'Oh, Marc,' Lee whispered, 'you're my life. Without you, I'm lost.' She reached up and wound her arms around his neck, pulling his face down close to hers. 'Kiss me, love me,' she begged with unconscious yearning, revealing without shame, 'I *need* you.'

There was strength and unconcealed passion in his response, a hunger that only she could assuage, and she almost cried out loud with the joy of it as his lovemaking took her to the heights of sensual ecstasy, and beyond.

Harlequin Plus

A WORD ABOUT THE AUTHOR

Helen Bianchin began scribbling in exercise books when she was twelve, but never with the conscious thought of becoming a writer. She gave serious attention to the idea only after the birth of her third child.

Her first romance novel was more than two years in the writing, and there was a further three months needed for her to gather the courage to send it off to a publisher.

Today writing is both a compulsion and a source of enjoyment for Helen Bianchin. "There is immense satisfaction in completing a novel," she explains, "but it doesn't take long before I'm drawn to the typewriter again. A name comes to me, a setting, and I turn it all over in my mind." And gradually another story begins to unfold.

Helen Bianchin was born in New Zealand, where she now makes her home. She and her husband, Danilo, are the parents of Lucia, Angelo and Peter.

Harlequin Presents...

Take these 4 best-selling novels FREE

That's right! FOUR first-rate Harlequin romance novels by four world renowned authors, FREE, as your introduction to the Harlequin Presents Subscription Plan. Be swept along by these FOUR exciting, poignant and sophisticated novels....
Travel to the Mediterranean island of Cyprus in **Anne Hampson**'s "Gates of Steel" ... to Portugal for **Anne Mather**'s "Sweet Revenge" ... to France and **Violet Winspear**'s "Devil in a Silver Room" ... and the sprawling state of Texas for **Janet Dailey**'s "No Quarter Asked."

Join the millions of avid Harlequin readers all over the world who delight in the magic of a really exciting novel. SIX great NEW titles published EACH MONTH! Each month you will get to know exciting, interesting, true-to-life people.... You'll be swept to distant lands you've dreamed of visiting.... Intrigue, adventure, romance, and the destiny of many lives will thrill you through each Harlequin Presents novel.

Harlequin Presents...

The very finest in romantic fiction

Get all the latest books before they're sold out!

As a Harlequin subscriber you actually receive your personal copies of the latest Presents novels immediately after they come off the press, so you're sure of getting all 6 each month.

Cancel your subscription whenever you wish!

You don't have to buy any minimum number of books. Whenever you decide to stop your subscription just let us know and we'll cancel all further shipments.

Your FREE gift includes

Sweet Revenge by **Anne Mather**
Devil in a Silver Room by **Violet Winspear**
Gates of Steel by **Anne Hampson**
No Quarter Asked by **Janet Dailey**

The compelling Irish Saga

The Defiant

MARY CANON

For centuries there has been
no love lost between the Irish
and the English. But for a brief
moment in time, at the court of
Elizabeth I, a forbidden love
was found...between a
steel-willed Irish spy and a
high-spirited English beauty..
Their love created
a powerful family,
and an even more
powerful legend.

1981
BEST
SELLER

FROM
WORLDWIDE LIBRARY